W9-CKK-317

THE BOOK OF
POWERFUL
SECRETS

IMPORTANT NOTICE

This manual is intended as a reference volume only, not as a medical guide or a reference for self treatment. You should always seek competent medical advice from a doctor if you suspect a problem.
This book is intended as educational device to keep you informed of the latest medical knowledge. It is not intended to serve as a substitute for changing the treatment advice of your doctor. You should never make medical changes without first consulting your doctor.

Printed in the United States of America
0 9 8 7 6 5 4 3 2 1

TABLE OF CONTENTS

INTRODUCTION

The book you are holding in your hands right now may be the only one like it in the world. This book, **Powerful Secrets That Will Change Your Life**, will do just that --change your life! Jam-packed within these pages are hundreds of little-known secrets which can powerfully influence your ordinary world, and perhaps change your life forever! This is not a book that is all things to all people, but **it is** a book that thousands of people will pick up to find the very thing they need to change the course of their life. In fact, the specific answers you have been looking for may be just a few pages away, or somewhere deeper within some part of this book. We hope you find them. We've certainly tried to cover all the bases. Let's talk about money. Could you use several thousand dollars in hard cash right away? Do you think you could have that sum in your hands by the end of this day? We'll introduce you to a man who did just that -- and we'll tell you exactly how he did it! You can easily be the person to follow in his footsteps. Do you want to save big bucks on your house payments?

We'll tell you how to do it. Do you want to make your car last 200,000 miles and beyond? It can! We'll tell you how. Do you want to slash your monthly grocery bill by 50 to 75 percent? In these pages, you'll find a detailed plan to do just that. How's your credit? Not too great? Well, you don't need credit to borrow money -- or get a credit card. We've looked into it and found a way that should work for you. No matter how bad your credit rating is, you can get a credit card. How can that be? You'll read all about it in the pages that follow. These are just a few of examples of the way this book will improve your financial condition. From the very basics, like cars and groceries, to leveraging serious credit, you'll find ideas in this book few have thought of before. All you have to do is put them to good use, and you can change your life! Let's talk about health. Do you want to melt 20 years from your life? Are you tired of seeing your face wrinkle and your waistline bulge? Do you want to stop the aging process dead in its tracks? This book will show you the way. Six months from now, you could look 10 years younger -- and not only look 10 years younger, but feel 10 years younger! One year from now, you can say goodbye to 20 years ... or more! Did you know that something as simple as the way you think about the passage of time can actually make you grow older faster? It can. In this book, we can teach you a way to "think" your rate of aging to a slower pace. It's part science, and part ancient wisdom. But the most important thing is that it works -- and that we spell it all out for you. Which foods can rid your body of harmful toxins? What kind of cheese prevents tooth decay?   How can you make your teeth whiter?   Can you lower your blood pressure without drugs or doctors? Can you finally give up those hateful cigarettes without pain, effort or will power? Can you grow hair on a bald head? We think you can. We'll introduce you to someone who's done it. We have found ways to do all of these things and more. Let's talk about lifestyle. Have you ever wanted to travel to the country of your dreams -- for FREE? You can! Where there's a will, there's a way. But you don't need "a will" because you have this book! By playing your cards right, you can arrange for a travel agency to fly you to any point on the globe you choose -- all at no cost. We'll tell you how.

How's your sex life? Drab? Boring? Completely nonexistent! It doesn't have to be that way. Having a great sex life may be as easy as clearing up a few minor problems, or by discovering (and solving!) major problems you never knew you had. And don't forget, you are never too old to have great sex. Even men in their 90's can still get a firm erection -- and do something with it. Read all about it here.   Would you like to further your education, or send your children to college without taking a dime out of your pocket? There are many more ways to do this than you might have imagined. Would you like to get out of that old beater that passes for a car and drive away -- today -- with the brand new car of your choice? There's a way. There's always a way. That's what this book is all about. It's about finding you a way -- a powerful way -- to get the

things you want out of life. In the pages of this book are answers --
detailed answers that you can use and profit from tremendously.
We've pulled out all the stops. We've invested hours of research
and scoured every conceivable source to make this book the most
complete and heretofore unpublished source of "insider information"
available anywhere. We hope that this book stimulates your mind.
We hope that it shows you a way to do something that you have
been unable to do in the past. Even if you don't find the specific
answer you need, perhaps the ideas you find here can jump-start
the possibilities for you. One idea leads to another, and that's what
this book is chocked full of: loads and loads of ideas. Ideas that
can work for you. One year from today, we hope this book will be
nearly tattered. We hope the pages will be ragged and dog-eared.
We hope you will use your highlighting marker freely. That means
you will have scoured every page and put much of the valuable
information you have found here to good use. If you do that, you
will have succeeded. Buying this book is only the first step.
Reading it is the second, and the third and most important step --
applying what you have learned in real life! So, come on! Turn the
page, start reading -- and change your life!

Aging

You Can Slow the Process to a Dead Crawl!
You Can ERASE decades of aging from your Body!

Don't think about dying. Instead, think about letting the aging process in your body die — while you remain youthful and vigorous for many decades to come.

Why not?

Is it possible? Is it possible to retain a youthful appearance and a feeling of vigorous good health well into your 60s, 70s, 80s, 90s ... even beyond?

Make no mistake about it. The answer is absolutely YES!

From a very young age, you have been conditioned to believe that everyone grows old sooner or later. Such a belief is planted so deeply within your mind that you have probably never questioned it. With all of your mind sold on the firm belief that you will grow old at a certain rate, is it any wonder that your body will follow suit?

But what if you began to challenge that belief today. What if you convinced yourself that you could live beyond 100, and not just live, but thrive with full use of your body and mind well into ages 120 or 130? Would it make a difference?

The answer lies in the fact that the body and the mind are not nearly as separate as we think they are. Your mind can not only control the outward movements of your body, but can also be taught to influence some of its deeper functions, including heart rate, blood pressure, temperature, even cellular function.

But before we get into some of the more esoteric, yet proven, ways you can stop the aging process, let's ease into it by first examining the ordinary, common things you can do to to stop growing older — and lift the years from your body.

Exercise: The Real Fountain of Youth?

Consider this true story:

Ray was 58 years old. At his 40-year high school reunion, he was shocked to find out that about half of the young men who had played with him on his high school football squad some 40 years ago were dead. Most had died from degenerative diseases, such as heart disease and cancer.

In light of the fact that 50 percent of his high school classmates were already dead, Ray felt lucky to be alive. He also felt lucky because he was no picture of health himself. He was about 40 pounds overweight. He had high blood pressure and smoked a pack of cigarettes per day. He drank more than he should, never exercised, and generally had a diet that consisted of meat and fried foods.

He had been one of the lucky ones. Most people who maintain such a lifestyle can't hope to live far beyond their sixties, and many die earlier.

Ray knew he was but two years away from 60, and that his chances of seeing 70 weren't so hot.

But Ray had a lot to live for. Three great children and a wife who still adored him after 29 years of marriage. He still liked his job, found it challenging, although stressful, and he also wanted to travel after retirement.

Ray decided to make some changes. He was determined to give up smoking and start up an exercise program. Back in high school, Ray had been a distance runner on the track team. Although he won few races, he always remembered how much he loved running — just running — feeling good as he breathed fresh air and watched the countryside go by.

At age 58 and hefting around an extra 40 pounds, there was no way he could "run," much less jog, not even across his back yard without gasping and breaking into a sweat. But Ray didn't let that get him down. He knew that 40 years of inactivity and cigarettes could not be undone overnight. He set a firm mental intention to build his way up slowly, no matter how long it took.

In the first week, Ray huffed and puffed around his yard. True, it was humiliating, even shocking, how little his body could do. But Ray had nothing to lose and everything to gain. He kept at his jogs around his yard for several weeks until he felt ready to try an entire neighborhood block.

Jogging nonstop around that first block was amazingly difficult, but equally satisfying. And already the changes had begun. Ray had dropped eight pounds in three weeks. He felt more clear-headed and energetic. He found less need of the stimulation of cigarettes and coffee. One success built upon another.

After four months, Ray had worked his slow jog up to a mile a day. His weight melted away from his body. He found giving up cigarettes a breeze once he began to breath more deeply and felt generally better about himself. His work became easier because his body was better at absorbing stress.

Just one month before his 60th birthday, Ray had lost the entire 40 pounds he had collected over the past four decades. The rosey color had returned to his face. He could run a 5 kilometer race like it was the length of his back yard. His appearance had changed dramatically. Although he was turning 60, it might just as well have been 40. There was no doubt, a daily program of running, eating healthy food and quitting a couple of bad habits had dissolved 20 years from Ray's body.

What can we learn from Ray's story? Plenty.

First, this case study shows us that there is no big secret to taking the years off your body. Ray didn't do anything that was particularly revolutionary. He started exercising every day, switched to a low-fat diet, and quit cigarettes. His reward for doing that was nothing less than beating a certain death sentence. Instead of having a heart attack at age 60, Ray made that milestone a new beginning for himself.

Beating the aging process can be a simple as knuckling under to common sense. Knowing what to do is not the problem. Finding the discipline to follow through is.

Most of you probably know that eating better and exercising will be good for you. But what you have to realize is that it will be better than good for you — it may literally transform your body and life into a whole new realm. It's amazing how sometimes miracles are floating all around us, and how we are just too foggy to plug into those miracles and take advantage of them.

Have no doubt about it, a simple exercise and healthy eating program is nothing less than a bona fide miracle waiting to happen to you.

There is more than anecdotal and circumstantial evidence that exercise can add years to your life and make you look younger. Scientists have been examining the effects of exercise on the body for decades and there is no longer any speculation about this: there is nothing better we can do for our bodies, there is no better anti-aging process than daily exercise.

It's never too late. You can be just like Ray. No matter how out of shape you are, even if you must start at the very bottom, you can begin today to turn back the hands of time. Start with five minutes a day. Work your way up to 10 minutes. Stick with it. As the days peel by, you'll soon be looking back and laughing at the old, out-of-shape, aging you. You'll looking the mirror and see a transformation take place day by day.

Vitamins That Slow the Aging Process

Most scientists still agree that taking antioxidants will help your body battle the aging process. What are antioxidants? They are substances which prevent runaway molecules in your body, called free radicals, from breaking down the fundamental integrity of your cells.

Where can antioxidants be found? In the vitamins A, C and E. By increasing your intake of these three vitamins daily, you may be striking a major blow against the ravages of time.

Be warned that taking large doses of vitamins A and E is not recommended. Doing so can have toxic side effects on your body. You can safely increase your intake of these two by about twice the recommended daily allowance. Check the label on the vitamin bottles for what the proper dosage is.

Vitamin C is another matter. It is difficult to overdose on vitamin C because your body metabolizes it like a food. The famous scientists and two-time Nobel Prize winner Linus Pauling consumes some 300 times the recommended daily allowance of vitamin C. When he develops a cold, he increases it until the illness passes. Pauling firmly believes that vitamin C is a "miracle drug."

Remember also that it is best to get your vitamins directly from natural sources, in other words, foods that are rich in vitamin A, C and E. There are many food rich in vitamin A and C, but finding vitamin E in ordinary foods is more difficult. For vitamin E, you may be best finding it in supplement form.

Studies Prove That Meditation Keeps You Young

Scientists now have proof that people who meditate just 10 minutes a day can slow the aging process of their bodies considerably.

According to the Journal of Behavioral Medicine, scientists recently compared the levels of an age-related hormone called DHEA-S (dehydroepaindosterone sulfate) in meditators to those of people who don't meditate.

In the study, the level of DHEA-S of 423 meditators was compared to that of 1,252 healthy non-meditators. The subjects were divided into groups according to their age. Meditators were compared to nonmeditators who were in the same age group.

Meditating females showed higher levels of DHEA-S levels than nonmeditatiing women in every age group. Men under age 40 showed little variation, but after age 40, meditators began to show significantly higher levels of the youth hormone than nonmeditators.

Scientists have also long noted that over a lifetime, people who have meditated for 10 years or more have lifespans that are 20 years longer on average than people who do not meditate.

What Kind of Meditation is Best?

No doubt, the word meditation has conjured up some scary or negative images in many of you. Perhaps you pictured Zen monks with heads shaved doing weird things in a monastery on some remote mountaintop, or long-haired, freaky hippy people smoking pot and sitting in a cross-legged position.

But not all meditation is so far out. In fact, meditation can be as simple as finding a quiet, undistracted place to sit while you calm down, count your breaths and clear your mind of your worries for 10 minutes each day.

Meditation is not necessarily associated with any particular religion, although many religions employ it as part of their practices. You can choose to meditate simply as a way to calm down and get control of your life.

It doesn't take a lot of time. You are not required to buy any expensive equipment. You don't need a teacher and you don't have to enroll in a class to learn how to do it better.

Here is an easy kind of meditation you can try, and which just about anyone can perform successfully:

(1) Find a quiet room where you will not be disturbed by people, telephones or distracting noise from televisions or radios.

(2) You can either sit in a chair or lie flat on your back with your arms at your side. If you sit in a chair, you should not slouch, but sit straight up so that your spinal cord is perpendicular with the floor and ceiling. A firm table chair is best. A soft chair or a soft bed to lie on may put you to sleep. You do not want to go to sleep.

(3) Once you have yourself positioned, you should take three deep breaths to relax. Tell yourself that you will relax a bit more after each deep breath.

(4) After the three breaths, you should start counting your breaths. Count one inhale and one exhale as one, the next inhale and exhale as two, and so on. When you get to four, start over with one and proceed again to four, and so on.

(5) You should keep as much of your attention as possible on your breathing. The object of meditation is to clear the mind, but the problem is, the more you try the harder it will be. A key is not to try too hard, or perhaps not to try at all, if that makes sense. Instead of trying to fight off your thoughts, just let them flow through your mind. Let them come and go without paying much attention to them. Just

keep reminding yourself that breathing is your primary concern right now. When your thoughts stray away and get caught up within themselves, gently but firmly bring your thoughts back to your breath counting.

(6) You may find this simple meditation deceptively difficult. Even if it's just for 10 minutes, keeping your mind clear is remarkably difficult to do.   Lots of thoughts are always crowding in and clamoring to be heard. But don't be daunted if you feel like you are not succeeding. It's the process itself that is what we are after, not the result. When it comes to meditation, the road itself is the goal, and not what lies at the end of the road.

That's it. If you set aside 10 minutes each day, or perhaps twice a day, and practice this simple breathing meditation exercise, you can add 20 years to your life.

It almost seems too simple, doesn't it? Well, Albert Einstein once said that it takes a genius to see the obvious. When it comes to meditation, you don't have to be a genius to do something that's incredibly simple, yet enormously beneficial to your overall life.

Your Friends will Keep You Young — Literally

If you live alone, without family or close friends, chances are that you will age much faster, and perhaps die years before your time.

Scientists at the University of Goteborg in Sweden recently studied a sample of 50-year-old men, giving each of them complete mental and physical examinations. Seven years later the researchers went back to find the men, and also looked up those who had died. What they found was that, among men who had died, all of them had reported before their deaths that they had few friends and little or no family support. In all, 11 percent of the 50-year-old lonely men were dead after seven years and only three percent of those who had friends and families to provide them with emotional support.

The scientists identified specific incidents in the lives of the lonely men who had died which indicated that they experienced significant stress about having to face problems alone. Some of the stressful events included being forced to move, feelings of insecurity at work, serious financial trouble and being the target of legal action.

The Swedish scientists concluded that the stress lowered the men's resistance to disease, and that the lack of loving caring people around them left them with less psychological "will" to fight off stress and disease.

Therefore, if you want to significantly increase your resistance to disease and aging, you should stop doing it alone. Now is the time to reconnect to your family or to go out and try to make a friend or two. It could add years to your life — years of happiness.

Looking Younger is Being Younger

There are many tricks, both big and small, that can take years off your appearance. The real biggie is, of course, cosmetic surgery (plastic surgery). But, the procedure is expensive and involves risks most of us prefer to avoid.

For women (and some men), make-up is the major device used to achieve a more youthful appearance. If it is applied with care, make-up is an effective tool. The trick is to choose the proper colors for you and then apply them with a light hand. Heavy make-up will NOT be effective in your quest for a youthful appearance. Choose colors that match your natural complexion. If you are in doubt, consult a make-up sales person. Most are happy to assist you free of charge, especially the independent retailer who works out of her home. Usually these people have had some training in assisting customers with color choices. In general, it is best to choose sedate colors; bright reds, blues, and greens can look artificial and add years instead of subtracting them. A foundation just slightly lighter than your natural coloring so that your own color glows through will look best.

Make your facial skin look its youngest and most vibrant. Keep it clean and moist. When you clean your skin, gentleness is the key word. Use a facial cleanser only once or maybe twice a day. Use a gentle cleanser. When you wash your face use your fingertips gently - don't use a washcloth. Blot it dry gently - don't rub it dry. While your skin is still damp apply a moisturizer. Most older people are afflicted with dry skin due to a slow-down in oil gland production. The dryness won't cause wrinkles, but will make them more noticeable. Many moisturizers are on the market. Some of the fairly cheap ones are effective. Glycerin is an effective ingredient, but there are other good ones as well.

Use a sunscreen if you will be outside. Exposure to the sun can cause mottling, wrinkling, roughening, discoloration, sagging, and cancer. Use a waterfast sunscreen of at least an SPF15 rating. Apply it to your skin liberally. It's best to apply it 15 minutes or so before going outdoors. Especially avoid the sun during it's peak period - from about 10 A.M. until about 2 P.M. Also be very careful of reflections from snow, sand, water, and other light colored surfaces. These surfaces intensify the sun's rays. Avoid the electric beach - tanning beds. Be careful to shade your eyes when you do go out in the sun. Squinting or other frequent contortions of your face will , over time, cause wrinkles or make those you have deeper. If you avoid the sun zealously, be sure that your diet includes enough Vitamin-D.

Vitamins that are important to maintaining youthful skin are beta-carotene, B Complex, A, and C. Eat plenty of fresh fruits, carrots, and green leafy vegetables.

Don't sleep on your face. Try to sleep on your back or in a position where your face will not be pushed up into wrinkling. Sleep wrinkles tend to last longer on older, less pliable skin. If you protect your face at night you may even find that some of your smaller wrinkles will vanish.

Exercise. Yes, exercise even helps reduce wrinkles. It promotes a healthier skin which is a more elastic skin.

Don't smoke and don't drink. Smoking decreases blood flow which is essential for healthy skin. Alcohol causes puffiness that stretches the skin. Eventually the swelling and shrinking of your skin will cause wrinkling.

Use a humidifier to keep the air in your house moist. Moist air is wonderful for your skin.

Toners and astringents can dry your facial skin. Be especially wary of those that have a high percentage of alcohol in them. If you have extremely oily facial skin these products are of some value, but for dry skin they can be detrimental.

Treat your facial skin gently and carefully, especially in the fragile eye area. To take off eye makeup, wipe gently with a cotton ball dipped in eye-makeup remover. Use similar gentle methods to remove the rest of your makeup. Pulling and stretching your skin can contribute to it's loss of elasticity.

A "chemical peel" can be done by your dermatologist. The process will "peel" the old, dead skin. New, more supple skin will replace it. Your new skin will look less wrinkled and more youthful. A peel doesn't take long to do, but there is a fairly long recovery period. Your skin will be sensitive and red for quite a while.

You can fight wrinkles with Retin-A, a drug available by prescription. It is applied to the skin. Retin-A can irritate the skin and cause it to become sensitive to the sun. You have to be very careful about exposure to the sun while you are using it. Alpha hydroxyl can also be effective.

Lac-Hydrin, also available by prescription, works to remove fine wrinkles and eliminate age-spots. It is a moisturizing lotion.

If you do not wish to visit the doctor, you might find you have good results with an over-the-counter exfoliating treatment. Use carefully. Be gentle with your skin!

Dermabrasion, a resurfacing of the skin, by stripping away the skin - kind of like sandpapering painted wood - can result in painful recuperation. It can also leave your skin permanently lighter or unevenly pigmented.

Drinking plenty of fluids will combat aging skin. You may think you drink enough, but WHAT you drink makes a difference. You need six to eight glasses of water or other noncaffeinated fluids a day. Those many cups of coffee won't do it. Alcoholic beverages don't count either. Water is extremely important - next to the air you breath, water is the most important element to your survival. If you don't drink enough water, you can end up with too much body fat, poor digestive efficiency, poor muscle tone, and water retention. Drinking plenty of water does a lot of good things for you. It'll help keep you young by combatting wrinkles and excess weight.

Next to your face, your hair is one of your most prominent features - often the first thing people notice about you. It can add years or subtract years from your appearance.

First, color. Gray hair DOES make you look older. There are many good, easy-to-apply hair color products on the market for both men and women. The real trick to using it to achieve a more youthful appearance is in choosing the color. As you grow older, you should choose colors lighter than the natural color of your youth. Darker colors will add years to your appearance. If you choose to go "naturally light," use a product to brighten nature's gift. A bright white is more youthful than a gray or yellowish white.

Second, style. A hairstyle swept up and away from your face and with a little height on top will make you appear younger. For men, the lengthening of the forehead created by a receding hairline often makes them look younger. Extensive balding cannot be hidden by growing your hair longer and combing those long strands across it; it only adds years to your appearance. Just cutting those strands will cut away years. Remember, a confident, matter-of-fact acceptance of baldness makes you attractive and sexy.

Both men and women can also use weight control to look more youthful. Most of us are aware that excessive weight can add years, but being too thin can do the same. As we grow older, moderation of weight is the key.

But, don't crash diet — that type of dieting makes you look tired and haggard, older. Diet sensibly.

Some foods will help keep you younger. Broccoli - the food that helps you fight cancer and heart disease - gives you doses of vitamin C and beta-carotene that will help keep skin smooth and youthful. Vitamin C builds up collagen and beta-carotene fights wrinkles. In addition, it is a good source of calcium - a necessary mineral to keep bones from becoming brittle. Cabbage has both vitamin C and beta-carotene and, like the broccoli is a very good source of calcium. Sweet potatoes are high in beta-carotene. Carrots are very high in beta-carotene and have been shown to cut stroke rates by over fifty percent. Strawberries, parsley, and bell peppers are all very high in vitamin C. You should eat your carrots cooked rather than raw to make their beta-carotene more easily assimilated in your body. Broccoli is best for you when it is raw, or microwave or stir fry it. Don't cut your sweet potatoes before baking. They will loose more than half of their vitamin C.

Now these foods should be included in your diet in generous

amounts. But don't eat a lot of just a couple of foods and eliminate everything else from your diet. A healthy diet consists of a large variety of foods. Go for a balanced diet with lower fats, sugars, and starches and more fiber. The healthy, sensible diet required to maintain a moderate weight will also add a youthful glow and energy. With the added energy, you will feel better about yourself and become more physically active which will change your attitude.

And, a change of attitude is probably the most important secret for men and women who want to look younger. If you think old, you will walk old, feel old, look old, BE OLD.

Practice thinking younger - change your attitude. Age has less to do with years than it has to do with attitude. When you accept this fact - when you truly believe this - your appearance will improve dramatically. Your posture will improve, and poor posture advertises advancing age. Your behavior will become more youthful. Your outlook will improve.

Remember your age is what you make it. John F. Kennedy didn't become president until he was 43-years old. And he was a YOUNG president. Henry Ford was 50-years old when he introduced the assembly line that lead to mass production of cars. At age 53, Margaret Thatcher became Britain's first female prime minister. At age 71, Golda Meir became prime minister of Israel. At age 80, "Grandma" Moses had her first one-woman art exhibit. At age 96, George C. Selbach scored a 110-yard hole-in-one. On his 100th birthday, Eubie Blake, a ragtime pianist and composer, said, "If I'd known I was gonna live this long, I'd have taken better care of myself."

It's never too late to have a happy, optimistic outlook, never too late to do something special - even if those special things are not recorded for posterity.

And a happy, optimistic outlook- looking at life as the adventure it is (at any age), taking an interest in the fascinating world around you, approaching the world with confidence - will be reflected in your appearance.

With a new attitude, you will choose clothing styles with a youthful flair. Take care not to choose EXTREMELY youthful styles, however. Childish styles on mature persons are as bad as the "grandma styles" that grandmas shouldn't wear. More youthful clothing styles will not only make you look younger to others but will make you feel younger.

With your new attitude will come facial changes. Confidence shows. Smiles truly do light up faces. A happy face is a younger face.

Best of all, with a new attitude you will not only look younger, you will feel younger. "You are only as old as you feel." So with a new attitude, YOU WILL BE YOUNGER!

These changes are easy to make once you begin. You see, it's a wonder cycle — each change encourages the implementation of another change. And each outer change brings about a change of the inner you, as well. Looking younger changes the way you feel about yourself and about the world.

When you "pep up" your appearance and your attitude, it will feel to you like the world around you has changed, too. You will experience a dramatic change in your life — and YOU made it happen.

Your Mind Can Make You Young ... or Old

Okay. We've talked about exercise, vitamins and meditation, and we stand by the advice we have given to you about those anti-aging factors.

But now it's time to discuss the ultimate arbiter of how old we get and how fast. It's your mind and your beliefs. If you firmly believe that you will not live far past age 65, will such an attitude contribute to a longer life? It's hard to see how it could.

People who "target" their own deaths often do things, mostly subconsciously, to ensure that their beliefs become reality.

But what if you had the firm belief implanted in your mind that you are destined to live past age 100? With this thought or belief deep within you, might not your body follow suit?

Scientific evidence suggests that this is exactly the case. Many studies have been done in which people have been blocked from seeing clocks and calenders for weeks at a time. Once they have been removed from the psychological aspects of knowing what time it is, all sorts of strange things start happening with their behavior.

For example, one woman geologist who had agreed to spend several months in an underground cavern away from clocks and the visual cycle of night and day found that she could stay awake and clear headed for days at a time without sleep. She would sometimes go for as long as two weeks without even a nap, and then sleep for eight to 10 hours before getting up again to go about her work for several more days without sleep.

Later, when researchers asked her how she managed to stay awake so long, she was surprised that she had done so at all. Since she had no clocks or daylight to go by, she assumed that her sleep patterns had not changed at all.

This story illustrates the fact that time is really nothing more than an illusion. Without clocks or calenders we would be a lot less focused on the passage of time. Without knowing how fast time is passing, we could not psychologically set up the rate at which we expect our bodies to age.

If you did not know your age how could you have a mid-life crisis? How would you know when it was time to retire? How would you know when it was time to "slow down." If you didn't know your age, how could you be concerned about the "fact" that the average age of death in males in the U.S. is 68 and of females is 72?

The answer is that you wouldn't know, and if you didn't know how old you were, you would probably never have a mid-life crisis. You would retire when you felt like it, or when you could afford to, and it's likely you would never slow down. If you didn't know the average age at which you could expect to die there is no way you could target your own death.

Here is the big lesson we can take away from all this: The rate at which your body ages is not determined by time — it is determined by your mind. Time is secondary to mind since time is an artificial creation of the mind.

You should not think of yourself in terms of a number or an "age." You should make a judgment on your physical condition based on how you feel. That old cliche "you are as young as you feel" is in fact the truth. Don't think of yourself as middle aged, old, or anything else. Think of yourself as a timeless human being that is existing on the Earth according to the whims of your own mind and perspective, and not by the whims of artificial clocks and calenders.

Back Pain

Today, millions of people have an age-old problem: chronic back pain. But did you know that this modern-day affliction has many ancient remedies — treatments which have withstood the test of time because they work!

You can give up on drugs which have limited effect and harmful side-effects; you can go back to performing tasks you gave up long ago; you can qualify for employment which your "bad back" has kept you from ... you can do all of this if you faithfully take a few minutes a day to practice the following exercises which have come down to us through the ancient Hindu practice of Yoga.

The following exercises go by many names, but they are most commonly known as The Snake, The Cobra, and The Insect. These exercises are more than just some air-fairy mystical remedies put forward by weak-minded New Agers. These exercises are also recommended by modern medical doctors and highly trained chiropractors. Let's take a look at them one at a time.

Preparation:

While these exercises are designed primarily to make your back feel better, there is a strong mental or psychological aspect involved with them. These exercises should be performed in a way that calms your mind and creates a general feeling of peace within yourself. Because of this, you should find a quiet place where you won't be disturbed by unnecessary noise, or other people. Make the 20 or so minutes you spend per day on these exercises "your time."

Also, wear loose-fitting clothing and prepare a padded but firm place for yourself on the floor. A blanket or a mat on a carpet should do nicely.

The Snake

(1) Lie flat on your stomach, hands by your side, feet together.

(2) Place your hands, palms down, besides your waist. Your fingers should be pointing forward.

(3) Inhale as you begin to lift yourself up on your hands, bringing the head back and arching the spine as far as it will go. (Note: Never force any part of your body further than it wants to go. If you begin to feel pain — you've gone too far!) Keep your legs straight. Don't bend your knees — you want to lift yourself up, kind of as if you were doing push-ups with paralyzed legs. Think of the way a cobra lifts its head up and leaves its body and tail on the ground.

(4) As you lift yourself up, you don't have to keep going until your arms are straight, but keep your pelvic area pressed firmly to the floor.

(5) Exhale. And lower yourself back down gently. Repeat the exercise a number of times. You will feel your tightness diminish with each repetition of the exercise. You should try to hold yourself in the upward position for about 15 seconds.

The Cobra

(1) Lie flat on your back with your arms at your sides.

(2) Slowly stretch out your arms from your sides, moving them above your head. Stretch your entire body this way while taking in a slow, deep breath as you suck in your stomach. Try to keep your mind calm and clear. Think only of the breath moving in and out of your body.

(3) Slowly put your arms back down to your sides as you exhale. Feel your entire body relax. Repeat the exercise as many times as you would like.

That's all there is to it. It's simple, but powerful. Your back will love you for it.

The Insect

(1) Lie on your stomach, hands by your side, palms up.

(2) Raise your head and place the front of your chin only on the floor.

(3) Make fists of your hands and place them under your thighs in your groin.

(4) Inhale, stiffen the body and push down on your arms. Bring your legs up in the back as high as they will go.

(5) Hold this pose for 15 seconds, or as long as you can while holding your breath.

(6) Exhale and lower your legs. Relax and repeat the exercise as often as you wish.

That's it! Perform all three of the above exercises on a regular basis once or twice a day, and you should experience a dramatic increase in your back strength, and an equally dramatic decrease in back pain.

One more excellent back-pain relief tip:

The following is not so much an exercise as it is a position. By assuming this position once or twice a day, you can allow your back to heal and grow stronger. Here's what you do:

Lie on your back and put your lower legs up on a chair. Your knees should point directly up at the ceiling. Your back and spine should be straight and firmly on the floor. That's all there is to it. Maintain this position for about 30 minutes. Spend the time relaxing and thinking calming thoughts. Try to ignore the chatter of your mind and focus your attention on your breathing. If you don't want to spend an entire half-hour in this position on the floor, try it for 15 minutes, or so, or assume the position whenever you feel back pain coming on. Stay in the position until you feel better.

A final note:

Don't perform any of the above exercises if they increase your pain.

Use Common sense. Be careful. More serious back problems may require the attention of a specialist.

Blood Pressure
High Blood Pressure: Causes and Effects

By now most of you are familiar with the "Silent Killer." It's high blood pressure, also known as hypertension. Hypertension is called the Silent Killer because there are millions of people out there right now who are walking around with dangerously high blood pressure — and they feel perfectly healthy.

But like a ticking time-bomb, people with high blood pressure could explode at any time. High blood pressure can lead to heart failure, a stroke or brain hemorrhage, and kidney failure.

Anyone can have high blood pressure, even people who are athletic and eat healthy diets. It's far more likely, however, that overweight people who smoke or drink too much will succumb to this serious illness.   Other major causes of high blood pressure are high amounts of stress in your life and heredity.

The First Step: Get Yourself Checked

About the only good way to find out if you have high blood pressure is to go somewhere to have it checked.   Some people with hypertension may have frequent headaches or nose bleeds, but the only sure way to measure your blood pressure level is to take a reading with a blood pressure cuff.

Fortunately, free blood pressure checks can be had just about anywhere. Most hospitals and clinics conduct free blood pressure check sessions. Many drug stores have blood pressure machines set up where you can get checked any time. Just call your local clinic or pharmacist for information on where you can have yourself checked out. Getting your blood pressure checked costs next to nothing, it's simple and painless. You have no excuse not to do it regularly.

See a Doctor

If you find that you have high blood pressure, don't take chances, see a doctor. If your blood pressure is high enough, you may need medication. But doctors and medicine should not be your only resource. There are many, many things you can do right now to get your high blood pressure under control. Let's go through them one at a time.

It's What You Eat and Drink ... and What You Don't

The Hidden Salt/Sodium Factor

Unless you have been living in a cave for the past two decades, you know that too much salt and sodium is one of the major causes of high blood pressure. So it's obvious that you have to avoid all the common salty food, such as soda, crackers, potato chips, salted peanuts, and so forth.

But there may be many foods in your current diet which contain large amounts of sodium — foods which you may never have suspected. For example, what about a bowl of cereal with milk? Would that be a good choice for someone with high blood pressure?

No! For one thing, plain old milk is naturally high in sodium. Of course milk is a healthy drink for many reasons — but not for someone who has high blood pressure. Cereals are also healthy for the most part, but there are many popular brands that are so high in sodium that you would hardly believe it. Perhaps the worst culprit is Cheerios, which has a sodium content higher than most snack foods — even potato chips!

It is not our goal here to go down the list of all the major breakfast cereals with high sodium contents. But the Cheerios example should put you on notice. From now on, check the ingredients labels carefully! Among the cereals lowest in sodium are Frosted Mini-Wheats, puffed rice, puffed wheat and shredded wheat.

There are many other foods besides cereals which have high sodium contents. Soups, soft drinks, eggs, many cookies and just about any other category of food you can think of may have large amounts of sodium or salt in them — even if they don't taste salty!

Remember that salt and sodium goes by many names. When you read the ingredient labels of food products watch out for these substances: Na, MSG (also know as monosodium glutamate), sodium citrate and nitrates. Avoid them all.

The Alcohol Factor

Some people think the very best thing to "calm the nerves" is a drink — a beverage with alcohol, that is. But alcohol will definitely not calm your blood pressure. It will make it worse! If you have high blood pressure and you have a drink or two every day, you are on dangerous ground. In fact any alcohol is never advised for people with high blood pressure.

It's Not All About Avoiding the Bad — It's About Eating the Good

Now the good news. So far we have been talking about all of the things that are bad for you, and what you should avoid. But lowering your blood pressure is not all about avoidance. Right now, we are going to tell you about two of the greatest natural weapons against high blood pressure. They are potassium and calcium. Sure, you heard of these before, but did you know that the latest scientific research has shown that increasing your intake of foods which contain high amounts of potassium and calcium can have a dramatic effect on your blood pressure?

Here are some common foods which are highest in potassium:

apricots	beet greens
cantaloupe	cod fish
collard greens	cowpeas
dates	flounder
kidney beans	lentils
orange juice	parsnips
potatoes	prune juice
pumpkin seeds	rhubarb
salmon	scallops
soybeans	tuna

Of course, there are other foods which contain potassium, but the items listed above are among the highest.

Calcium:

As we have told you, people with high blood pressure should avoid much milk because it is naturally high in sodium. Unfortunately, milk is perhaps the best source of calcium around. But don't worry, there are many other excellent choices for sources of calcium. Here they are:

sardines with bones	bok choy
pink salmon with bones	mackerel
baked beans	okra
broccoli	tofu
mustard greens	oysters
turnip greens	scallops
kale	soybeans
yogurt	beet greens

Note: Many antacid pills contain calcium, but they also tend to be very high in sodium! So before you go for the calcium in supplement form, check the sodium content!

You Must Lose Weight!

You can take many steps to lower your blood pressure, such as adjust your diet, avoid alcohol and stress, but it all may be for nothing if you don't control your weight. Obesity combined with high blood pressure is a very lethal combination. Losing weight will almost always have a dramatic effect on your blood pressure level. The more you lose, the more control you will tend to have.

Of course, losing weight is not as easy as waving a magic wand across your body and watching the pounds disappear. Also, the latest research seems to indicate that starvation diets are of little lasting help. All the weight you lose by starving yourself tends to return a short time after you have lost it.

It's a better idea to make changes in your diet based around getting more of the healthy things you need, such as potassium and calcium. Try adjusting your diet, say, for one month and put an emphasis on fruits and vegetables. Eat all you want — as long as you do not eat fats and sugar!

We are not suggesting that you necessarily have to become a

vegetarian, but you should be aware that in studies conducted over many decades and with thousands of people, it has been shown again and again that vegetarians have far less incidence of high blood pressure than do regular meat eaters.

The bottom line on the weight factor as it pertains to high blood pressure is this: don't worry too much about dieting, per se. Instead, favor those foods high in calcium and potassium, and just eat more fruits and vegetables in general. That will take you a long way toward controlling the deadly problem of hypertension.

Meditation — Is It The Ultimate Blood Pressure Control Method?

Last but not least, we must consider the power of the human mind and the true power it has over our physical bodies. The fact is, many very scientific studies have shown that just 10 to 15 minutes a day of meditation can have an astounding affect on your blood pressure.

You don't have to shave your head or join a Zen monastery to meditate. Simply sitting in a comfortable chair, clearing your mind of everything and concentrating on nothing else but your breathing for 10 to 15 minutes every morning and evening is all it takes.

Be warned — sitting quietly for even 10 minutes without thinking about your life and problems can be extremely difficult! Clearing the mind is no easy task — as you will see. But meditation is not about results — it's about process. Don't worry about how well you are doing it, or if you are doing it "right." Just the fact that you are taking the time to calm your mind twice a day can work miracles in your life. Try it! All you have to lose is 15 minutes a day —and you have your total good health to gain!

In summary ...

By eating right, avoiding toxic habits like drinking and smoking and by exercising and meditating, you may be able to control your blood pressure completely without drugs or doctors.

Miracle Foods

What food can you eat that will actually burn the fat from your body?

How about foods that will expel toxins and pollutants from your body? What process can stop hair loss, and even rejuvenate your hair growth? What food actually prevents tooth decay when it makes contact with your teeth? What foods can reduce your arthritis pain by 50 percent or more? Which combination of common vegetables' substances can help you cast off ugly cellulite just by applying them to your body on a regular basis? What vitamins can prevent you from ever getting cancer?

There are many foods which certain cultures have known about for centuries for their curative and restorative powers, but have been largely forgotten today because of our total dependence on modern Western science. Today, we have come to believe that if something is not scientific or technological, it must be of limited value.

That's simply not true. It's time we took a second look at some of the incredible powers available to us through certain foods, herbs and spices — safe alternatives to drugs and remedies which produce real results.

Let's start out with a common affliction that afflicts millions of people in the USA and around the world. It's the painful disease of arthritis.

All of the following and special preparations have been identified with helping or healing arthritis. You can find all of these items in any health food store. Search them out and be sure to try them consistently for at least three months.

Devil's Claw	Tumeric
Bilberry	Hawthorne
Bromelain	Hawthrone Berry
Burdock Root	Yucca Powder
Sarsaparilla Root	Ginger Root
Willow Bark	Ginseng

Most of the above are available in capsule or pill form. You can also find them in their raw form and use them in recipes of all sorts.

Foods which have been shown to have significant anti-inflammatory effects are:

Pineapple	Pineapple juice

Garlic	Brazil Nuts
Herring	Salmon
Onions	Broccoli

Make a major effort to include large amount of these foods in your weekly diet. You should try several or all of them in your diet almost every day. Remember that there are many garlic supplements on the market these days so that you can get the benefits of this wonder substance without its strong taste and bad breath.

Don't forget the fish

There is solid evidence to suggest that certain fish oils suppress the symptoms of arthritis. The fish oil identified as being particularly helpful is omega-3, and is found in freshwater fish, especially salmon. You can also get omega-3 supplements in health food stores. Eating fish is a better way to get your omega-3, however.

It's as much as what you don't eat

It's not enough to include the above food in your diet to battle arthritis. If you are suffering from any form of arthritis, there may be elements of your diet that are not only making your disease worse, but may actually be causing it. By eliminating these substances from your diet, you may reduce your symptoms by 50% to 100%!

Coffee

This is perhaps one of the worst possible substances for people with arthritis. Coffee is highly acidic and contains many bitter oils that can lead to inflammation even in people who do not have arthritis.

The caffeine in coffee contributes to stress and nervousness — both major culprits in increasing the pain and degenerative process of arthritis.

Milk

You would think that something as healthy as milk for your bones would be the exact thing needed for arthritis, but milk, in fact, has been pinpointed as a cause of joint inflammation in many people. You should try giving up all dairy products for a month or so and see what happens. That means avoiding dairy in all foods, including cookies, cakes, puddings and anywhere else you might find it.

Sugar

One of the primary reasons you should give up sweets if you have arthritis is that sugar can feed certain harmful bacteria in your intestines which will turn that sugar into harmful toxins. Certain types of yeast cells are the primary problem. By starving them of the sugar they need to thrive, you could significantly improve your symptoms by ridding your body of these microscopic parasites. Giving up sweets will also help you lose weight, which can ease the stress of arthritis.

Fatty Foods

It seems like every few months a new study comes out which supports the idea that fatty food, especially fatty meats, are a major contributor to arthritis pain.

In the latest study, 46 arthritis sufferers cut the fat in their diets so that only 10 percent of their total calories came from fat. They also reduced their total caloric intake by 30 percent. While they trimmed their diets, they took up exercise programs which had them walking four times a week for twenty minutes. Stress reduction classes were part of the program as well. The result was a very significant improvement in all aspects of the disease — less stiffness, less swelling, less fatigue, less morning stiffness and less pain.

Significantly, many of the study participants were able to cut back on the amount of prescription drugs they were taking, thus reducing harmful side effects. So the benefits of a low-fat, high vegetable diet go beyond their direct effects.

If you are an arthritic, making a strong but gradual effort to shift your diet from meat dominant to vegetable dominant could change your life — it really could!

Hair Loss

Doing something about baldness is a multi-million dollar industry. You've heard about most of the standard approaches — rugs, lotions, transplants and so on.

We could have offered you more of the same, but in our research for this book, we really wanted to explore some new territory in the search for a baldness cure. We didn't want to rehash the same old techniques. We wanted to offer you something you couldn't get in any other book, but we also wanted to find a new and real solution to putting hair back on a person's head.

We think we struck pay dirt. Listen to this amazing true story:

A doctor was visited by a man who was very depressed by his male pattern baldness. For this man, being bald was nothing less than a major physical deformation. He was so ashamed of his receding hairline that he had paid more than $5,000 for a transplant, which failed to take hold. Hairs that were transferred from his chest to his head fell out just as readily as his original hair had done.

In short, the balding man had been through all the standard treatments, from toupees to Rogain and hormone treatment.

The doctor sensed a strong psychological element in this particular man's predicament. Many men go bald and learn to live with it — and many men look even better with no hair. Yule Brenner and Michael Jordan are excellent cases in point. The same was true for the man in our case study. But in his mind, going bald was nothing short of a personal disaster.

The doctor then decided to try something revolutionary — yet completely safe. Recognizing that the man had powerful emotions associated with his baldness, the doctor decided to attempt to those harness emotions toward a positive end.

Emotions, in fact, represent mental energy, whether they are good or bad, and it is our belief system which determines to what end the energy of emotions will be used.

The doctor told the man that he had been working with a new, experimental form of radiation that was somewhat risky, but so powerful that it might rejuvenate the hair follicles on his scalp.

He put the man in a darkened X-ray room, told him to remove all of his clothes and lie flat on a table. The doctor then made some of the equipment hum, buzz and click — but in fact did nothing. No real X-rays or radiation of any kind was put into the room.

After the "treatment" the doctor told the man that he should see hair growth within a week or two.

Six months later, the doctor got a letter from the man. He was ecstatic. Included with the letter was a photograph of him with a full head of thick, wavy, black hair! All of his hair had grown back, and better than ever! The man hailed the doctor as a genius and thanked him to the point of slobbering embarrassment.

What had happened? Well, the simple and powerful truth is that this man grew hair with the power of his mind. By instilling deeply within him the belief that he could grow hair — he did.

Deepak Chopra, the Indian born American doctor who has written extensively on the power of mind over the physical body, says that each one of us has a natural "pharmacy" within our own bodies which can produce any substance it wants. In his recent book "Quantum Healing" he wrote:

"...we already know that the living body is the best pharmacy ever devised. It produces diuretics, painkillers, tranquilizers, sleeping pills, antibiotics, and indeed everything manufactured by the drug companies, but it makes them much, much better. The dosage is always right and given on time; side effects are minimal or nonexistent; and the directions for using the drug are included in the drug itself, as part of its built-in intelligence."

The point of all this is, if there is a drug that can grow hair on your head, it can certainly be manufactured within your own body — if you set your mind to the task. The fact that the balding man in our story did is proove that our bodies have the abilities to do what we command them to do, as long as our belief system goes along with it.

If you have a problem with a receding hairline, we suggest you take 15 minutes a day, perhaps a few minutes just before bed each night, to visualize the interior pharmacy of your body manufacturing the chemicals you need to grow hair. You don't have to be a chemist, or have the ability to picture the formation of complex molecules within you. Do it in your own way. Your mind is highly conducive to symbolic suggestion, so if you visualize millions of tiny hair-growing molecules surging into your scalp where they stimulate hair growth, that may be all you need to do. However you picture it will be the right way.

You can do it! You have the power in your mind to command your physical body to take the shape you want it to. As the famous author Richard Back once said: "Your body is an expression of your thought." Think about what you want your body — and hairline to be — and don't be surprised if it doesn't follow suit.

Foods Which Prevent Tooth Decay

Although these foods are extremely common, everyday foods, they deserve their status as "miracle foods" because they have been scientifically shown to significantly prevent tooth decay.

The first is the good old apple. An apple a day will keep the doctor away, and it will also keep tooth decay at bay.

Dentists have long touted apples for their tooth-cleaning properties. The idea was really put to the test at the University of Oslo in Norway. Researchers J.M. Birkeland and L. Jorkjend lined up a group of children and had some of them eat a bun, and others eat a bun and an apple. Less food stuck to the teeth of the apple eaters, clearing away food debris, and thus reducing the amount of decay due to excess bacteria from left-over food.

The second miracle food for tooth-decay prevention is one that compliments apples quite well — certain kind of hard cheese.

Yes, hard cheeses, especially Cheddar, contains enzymes which neutralize the harm done by decay-producing acids in the mouth. Studies done at the University of Rochester confirm the ability of cheese to kill harmful teeth-busting bacteria. Although cheese is high in sodium and fat, and probably not good to eat in significant quantities, studies show that just an ounce or so every other day can have a beneficial effect on clearing away harmful teeth bacteria.

Is This The Ultimate Cellulite Rub?

It's time to say good-bye to cellulite forever! Cellulite is the ugly, cheesy build-up of fatty skin cells on specific parts of the body — especially in females. Cellulite tends to gather on the thighs and on arms, but can also grow on the stomach, back and even on the neck.

But now, revealed here for the first time anywhere, is a simple preparation of oils and vegetables that hundreds of people have tried with tremendous results. By applying this preparation once a day in combination with a 20-minute massage of the affected area, you will see cellulite disappear within just a few weeks.

Prepare the following combination of ingredients:

1 cup of cold-compressed sesame seed oil
1 ounce of filtered garlic oil
1 tablespoon of baking soda
1 teaspoon of red or cayenne pepper

Mix the ingredients thoroughly and apply directly to the area of cellulite build-up and massage for 15 to 20 minutes every day. You must be persistent with the application over a period of six weeks. Don't miss a day! The rub will help scrub away the individual skin cells which congregate to make up cellulite.

How well does this preparation work? Well, we have gathered hundreds of testimonial from people who claim this spicy ointment is the best skin-care remedy since the invention of sunscreen. The only downside to the preparation is that many people with sensitive skin may have a harsh reaction to the garlic and red pepper, but most seem to tolerate the mixture extremely well.

This is an inexpensive, completely safe, natural remedy that you can most likely throw together right now with what you have in your kitchen cupboard. An important note: do not substitute any other kind of oil for sesame oil. That could add to your cellulite problem. Sesame oil is the only kind of oil that is completely neutral in terms of the Ph balance of your skin, leaves no greasy residue and will not leave and unpleasant odor.

Try this terrific cellulite remedy! You have nothing to lose — except gobs of hideous cellulite.

Foods that Help You Burn Fat

Okay, here we go again. Another diet plan ... this one added to the several billion other diets floating around out there in fat land.

You would rather not hear about another diet plan, right? Don't worry, we won't insult your intelligence with that kind of thing.

No, we're just going to give you a few bona fide, powerful tips on how to lose weight — tips that work, plain and simple.

You want to lose weight, right? Well, you can do it, but no matter what you do, you can't avoid the laws of physics. To lose weight, you must make your body lose mass by making it work harder physically. To keep the mass at a minimum, you can't keep adding to it without some kind of limit.

The bottom line? You must exercise more and eat less fat.

Notice we did not say eat less. It may seem contrary to the laws of physics that you can eat more and still weigh less, but there is a way to do it. All you have to do is make sure that the foods you eat do not have high percentages of fat as part of their total make-up. Here is an easy formula you can use to calculate the amount of fat in foods:

(1) Each gram of fat contains about 9 calories. Each gram of protein and carbohydrate contain about 4 calories. For example, a package of luncheon meat may tell you that each slice of meat has 170 calories, from 7 grams of protein, 1 gram of carbohydrate and 15 grams of fat.

(2) Multiply 15 grams of fat by 9 (because each gram of fat has 9 calories). The result is 135 calories from fat.

(3) Divide total calories, which is 170, into fat calories. In this case it would be 170 divided by 135, which equals 0.79.

(4) Multiply this figure by 100. The answer tells you that 79 percent

of the calories in that slice of meat comes from fat — not a very good percentage for someone trying to lose weight.

Using this formula, you can take the information listed on the labels of the food you buy and figure out the fat content for everything you eat. As a general rule, you should never eat anything that has more than 30 percent of its total content made up from fat. Obviously, the lower the fat content, the better off you will be.

It won't take you long to identify some of the things you like the best, which also have the least fat. These include leafy green vegetables, tofu, nuts and seeds, citrus and other fruits, beans, peas, rice and root foods, like carrots and potatoes. You can eat all you want of these foods and still lose weight! If you combine these foods with even moderate exercise, the fat will fly off your body.

There really is no secret to dieting. It's elementary physics. While you are losing weight, burn more than you take in. Once you have reached an optimum weight, never put more in than you intend to take out. It's that simple. It really is. So what are you waiting for?

Foods Which Eliminate Toxins From Your Body

We live in a poisonous society. Every day, we come into contact with high levels of synthetic chemicals and industrial pollutants which can build up in our body and cause major health problems. Auto emissions, pesticides, herbicides, factory pollutants. Make no mistake about it, these substances can drag down our health, slowly but surely. Some can even lead to death.

Toxins can lead to dozens of little, persistent health problems. Lots of colds, infections, aching muscles, low energy, and more. That's because your immune system has to work harder to fight off pollutants, diminishing the amount of attention it can spend on fighting off common, everyday diseases.

You can take action to rid your body of harmful toxins. By eating specific foods, fasting and doing what you can to eliminate your contact with all possible toxins in your environment, you can dramatically improve the way you feel, or even solve persistent health problems.

A Purifying Diet

A diet to eliminate toxins should have little or no animal products. Excluding these will reduce the amount of saturated fat you take in. Fat is one of the primary storage vessels for harmful substances in your body. What you should be eating is fruits, vegetables, beans, nuts and seeds. These will provide all the nutrition you need without the fat. They will also provide you with a high fiber diet, which is essential for eliminating unwanted substances from your intestines.

Perhaps the number one detoxifying food is brown rice. By adding brown rice to your diet everyday, you can make great headway in cleaning out your system.

Salt, sugar, alcohol, and food additives should be eliminated from your diet as much as possible. In addition, you should drink large amounts of water each day — preferably distilled or purified water. Other things you can do without are coffee and tea, which do nothing constructive for your body. The short-term stimulation caffeine laden drinks provide is not worth the long-term unbalances they produce.

Fasting

It has long been known that one of the best way to shed unwanted toxins from the body is to fast. Fasting is tough to do. It takes hard discipline and will power. It can also add a lot of stress to your life if you have a busy job and an active life. You should never try to fast while you are under a lot of stress and have a lot of important work to do.

But finding a time when you can spend a few restful days fasting will help clean out your body. You should start out by fasting for no more than 24 hours. You can eventually build your way up to 3 to 5 days, but you need a lot of practice before you should attempt that.

A decision to fast should never be made on your own. Always consult your doctor before you go on a fast.

Fasting will help many body systems, including digestion, circulation, sleep and mental acuity. You may also feel surges of spiritual or loving energy as you get into your fast. Also, fasting can relieve depression, mental anxiety and promote a general feeling of well being.

One of the most popular kinds of fasts — and one of the least dangerous — is the fruit-juice fast. In this fast, the person drinks large amounts of water and a moderate amount of fruit juice. Some fasters mix water with fruit juice. Some people consider eating nothing but fruits and vegetables to be a fast, but a real fast involves eating no solids at all.

Never fast without drinking lots of water! Your body can do okay without food for a day or two, but it can never go without water for an entire day.

Be warned that fasting can cause weakness, fatigue, irritability, anemia and other disorders. So be careful. Use common sense. If you start feeling ill, knock it off and have something light to eat, preferably some fruit to get yourself back into digestion slowly.

Anti-Cancer Vitamins

We are here now going to reveal the name to you of a substance so powerful, so far-reaching in its effect and so beneficial to your health, it could truly be called a miracle drug. What is this marvelous substance?

It's vitamin C.

Did you know that most animals on the planet produce their own vitamin C within their bodies naturally, but humans do not? Because of this, we need to get this vital nutrient through our diets. When we don't do that, the result is disaster. Total vitamin C deprivation can result in scurvy, a disease contracted by many sailors in times past after months at sea with no fresh vegetables to eat.

Total deprivation is one thing, but not getting enough vitamin C can cause problems as well. It can leave our body less capable of fighting off all manner of germs, bacteria and viruses. Not getting enough vitamin C will lead to more colds and infections, and may also make you more vulnerable to cancer.

Many studies both in and out of the laboratory have shown that vitamin C may be a significant agent for the prevention of all sorts of cancer. It also protects the body against environmental toxins, such as pollution, smoking and radiation therapy.

But there's more. Vitamin C is now being looked to as a possible substance for treating cardio-vascular disease, diabetes, gallstones, eye diseases, mental disorders, asthma, allergies and spinal-disc degeneration.

Vitamin C can help wounds heal faster and it can increase your resistance to mental and physical stress.

Whew! Now can you see why we call this stuff a "miracle" drug?

One of the best things about vitamin C is that you can take it in large doses without harmful side effects, as mega-doses of other vitamins can have. The brilliant scientist and two-time Nobel Prize winner Linus Pauling consumes 18,000 mg of vitamin C daily, which is 300 times the recommended daily allowance. He says if more people would do so, there would be far fewer diseases and a lot less reliance on drugs and therapies.

If you want to increase your general level of health, or if you want to fight off a cold or more serious illness, you can hardly go wrong by stepping up your intake of vitamin C. While taking vitamin C supplements is a good way to do that, its always better to go directly to those foods which are rich in vitamin C.

Here are foods which are highest in vitamin C:

broccoli	mustard greens
brussels sprouts	oranges
cooked cabbage	papaya chunks
cantaloupe	pineapple juice
cauliflower	spinach
collard greens	strawberries
grapefruit	turnip greens
mango chunks	tomato juice

Eat all you can of these foods - and all fruits and vegetables, and you will significantly increase your daily vitamin C intake, and more importantly, increase your resistance against a variety of deadly diseases, including cancer.

A final note about vitamin C: As we told you, your body cannot manufacture its own vitamin C. It also cannot store it. Once your body absorbs and burns up the vitamin C you eat, it's gone! Taking your vitamin C throughout the day, rather than just once a day, will ensure that you have some of the stuff in your body at all times.

Vitamin E

Like vitamin C, vitamin E is an antioxidant. An antioxidant is a substance which cleans what are called "free radicals" from your body. A free radical is a molecule that can have a destructive effect on the basic building blocks within the cells of your body.

Because vitamin E is an antioxidant, it can help prevent cancer, heart disease and other immuno-deficiency disorders. Vitamin E also keeps cholesterol and polyunsaturated fats from breaking down into harmful substances in the body.

Vitamin E has also been singled out as a substance which can improve circulation and prevent blood clots. It's antioxidant properties may slow the aging process and protect you against harmful environmental pollutants.

Vitamin E may be especially important for women. Studies show that it can lessen the pain of fibrocystic breast disease, prevent miscarriages, pregnancy complications, and relieve premenstrual problems.

Finally, some studies now suggest that vitamin E can prevent cataracts.

Where can you find vitamin E in foods? That's not easy. Most of the foods with vitamin E have high fat contents. It's probably best that you get extra vitamin E from supplements — but don't megadose! Taking large amounts of vitamin E is not as safe as vitamin C. Just taking one or two vitamin E tablets per day will be of benefit enough.

Vitamin A

Vitamin A is also one of the "Big Three" when it comes to cancer and aging prevention. Like E and C, vitamin A is an antioxidant which can scrub your body of harmful pollutants, as well as aid in the repair of your body's cell structure.

Many of you may know about this vitamin's important role in maintaining healthy skin. But it also has been identified as a source for treating peptic ulcers and promoting the healing of cuts and wounds.

Taking vitamin A in large quantities is definitely not advised, however. Mega-doses of vitamin A can actually harm your skin, cause liver damage and lead to migraine headaches.

It's probably best to get you vitamin A by eating those foods which are rich in the substance. Here are the best foods for vitamin A:

apricots	peaches
beet greens	spinach
bok choy	potatoes
cantaloupe	pumpkins
carrots	squash
kale	mixed vegetables

Generally speaking, fruits and vegetables which are yellow or orange in color are high in vitamin A.

So there you have them ...

Scientists and nutritional researchers agree that vitamins A, C and E are the "Big Three" when it comes to prevention of cancer, heart disease and the aging process. So valued are these three that many companies now package them in single, easy-to-eat capsules so that you get all three in by swallowing one pill.

You will be best off, however, by increasing your intake of the natural sources of these foods. The only exception is vitamin E, which can best be added to your diet in supplement form. In addition to getting a more potent source of the vitamin from their natural source, many of the foods which contain vitamins A and C are also high in fiber and beta-carotene, another source of anti-aging substances.

Energy

Are you tired and worn out all of the time?

Do you wish you had the energy you had ten years ago? Do you wonder what happened to your energy? And what you can do to get it back?

To lick the problem, it is necessary to track down the cause of your lack of energy. There are many things that could be causing your reduced energy level.

First, if you aren't getting enough sleep, it will tap your energy. Many of us don't get enough sleep most of the time. As we get older, we may find we need more sleep than we did in our teens. With the everyday demands of jobs and family plus the worry of keeping the bills paid, we may be getting less sleep than ever. If this is your problem, then, of course, the solution is in finding the time and worrying less so you can sleep.

Make a good night's sleep a priority. Look over the tasks you are attempting to accomplish each day. Eliminate some of them from your schedule. You are not a super-person. Not everything you do is absolutely necessary. Stop and think about it. Some things must be done every day, others you can do less often. Cut some things out of your schedule or delegate some of the tasks to another family member.

Maybe you are so bogged down with commitments that you feel unable to cope. You feel you are out of control and don't know where to start. Make some lists of the tasks you feel you must do. Make a priority schedule. Start the most important project, then work your way through them. As you check off each item, you will find yourself with a sense of control. When you feel in control of your life, you will feel more energetic.

Don't let yourself feel pressured into doing things. Learn to say "no." If you feel uncomfortable with that, learn to say "Let me check my schedule" or "Let me check with my spouse" and "I'll get back to you." When people ask you to volunteer for a project or invite you to a social function, use those phrases. It'll buy you some time to really look at your schedule. It'll be easier to decline gracefully later - when the pressure is off.

If worrying about the bills is keeping you from getting the rest you need, train yourself to put it out of your mind. Worry accomplishes nothing - things don't get better just because you worry about them.

Once you accept that fact and see the total waste that worrying is, it will be easier to let go of it. If you find you must worry, set aside 15 minutes well before bedtime to devote to worrying. If it's worth doing, it's worth scheduling time for it.

Also cut out the caffeine in the evening. Even if caffeine has never kept you awake before, it could be the culprit now. Omit the alcohol in the evening, too, for the same reason.

If you are certain you are getting enough sleep but still feel a lack of energy, look at your eating habits. Be sure that weight loss diet you are on isn't too stringent. You need a balanced diet, even if you are trying to lose weight. On the other hand, if you are eating a large meal shortly before going to bed, that can sap your energy, too.

Are you on drugs? Check with your doctor or pharmacist. Maybe your energy loss is a side effect of the drugs you are taking. Many drugs will do that to you.

Check out your bedroom. Make sure your bed is comfortable. Wear comfortable, loose clothing to bed. Place all clocks with their face away from you when you are in your bed. You don't want to be continuously checking the time. The room itself should be pleasing to you - whatever makes you comfortable - nothing that stirs up your emotions or makes you tense.

Look at your exercise program. You need a moderate amount of exercise for energy. But be sure that you don't exercise vigorously just before bedtime. Exercise can be overdone, too. If you overdo it, you can feel tired and dragged out.

Make sure your blood iron is up to par. Low blood iron will result in chronic fatigue. Your doctor can check it out with a simple test. The treatment is simple, too. Just take iron tablets or a multivitamin with iron.

Your thoughts and attitude can sap your energy. Fatigue can stem from depression. Sleeping poorly is often a part of depression. Even if you've been sleeping more, depression can upset the quality of your sleep. You can sleep until noon and still feel fatigued. If your depression is bad enough to upset your rest, it's time to do something about it. Find out what is causing you to feel depressed and change it. Or see someone who can help you.

You're not clinically depressed but just not very enthusiastic about anything? Well, that too will zap your energy. You need to find something to put some interest in your life. Eliminate some of the things you don't like to do, and then set some new goals to work toward. Take a few minutes to sit down and list some things you like to do. List somethings you think you're interested in. Look over the lists and set some goals or plan some hobbies in line with your interests. Get excited about it.

Are you in a rut? Bored? Make some changes in you life. Change your schedule. Take a little vacation, even if it's just for the weekend. Just small changes can jar you loose from the old rut and spark a new interest in life.

You feel old or think you're old? That kind of attitude can drain your energy. Work on looking younger and spice up your marriage and your sex life. You will find some helpful advice on that elsewhere in this book. Get enthusiastic.

What colors are you living with? Add some color to your life. Or change the colors in your life. Pink can sap your energy, make you passive. If you are living with pink try changing the color to blue. Blue will give you a feeling of power. Other colors elicit other emotions. Try changing the colors that surround you.

Try changing your light bulbs. Studies have shown that working under regular light bulbs may reduce efficiency. Try living under cool white fluorescent bulbs instead of the regular light bulbs.

Light is a time clock for your body. It may be that your body is confused about the time and doesn't really wake up. Drag yourself out of bed in the morning at a reasonable hour, and immediately plunge yourself into sun. Spend a couple of hours outside in the morning. Then wear dark glasses at night to tell your body night is here. Don't expect to see results immediately. You have to continue this routine for several weeks for it to be effective. If you live in an area where you get little sunshine substitute high-intensity, full-spectrum fluorescent bulbs for the sunshine. Ask your doctor to recommend the best type of bulb for you.

Lack of energy could be a sign of something seriously wrong with your health. Some of the health problems associated with chronic lack of energy are: diabetes, sleep apnia, mononucleosis, thyroid disorder, infection, heart disease. Your lack of energy could be a warning, and perhaps the only warning, of the onset of a disease. Check with your doctor if your weariness persists for a month or two.

Your Heart

We are all aware of the benefits of not smoking to reduce the risk of heart attack. If you don't smoke, don't start. If you do, you should consider quitting.

Many people, however, are unsure of what else they can do to cut their risk of heart attack. There are many things you can do.

Maintaining a low fat / low cholesterol diet throughout your life even if you are not in the "at risk" category is a good policy. It is difficult to maintain this diet but even cutting back is a help in reducing your risk of heart attack. The diet consists of a lot of "avoids."

Avoid over-using dairy products. Cream and most cheeses are high in cholesterol. Use skim or one percent milk. Much of the appeal of whole milk is simply that you are used to it. After using milk with less butterfat in it, you may find you prefer it. It is less cloying in your throat and, therefore, more refreshing.

Another thing to limit in your diet is egg yolks. You may have heard that eggs are high in cholesterol, but that is not quite true. It is the egg yolk only that you need to limit. Egg whites are OK. Sometimes you can make substitutions. If a recipe calls for two or three eggs, try one whole egg and two or three whites. If you are making scrambled eggs, taking out some of the yolks works just fine.

Avoid fried foods. They are high in fat and calories. Look for products with a low percentage of saturated fat. It's very important to avoid saturated fat. It is better to substitute products that have unsaturated fats in them. Also totally avoid products that contain or are fried in palm oil or coconut oil. Although these oils do not actually have cholesterol in them, they prompt your body to produce cholesterol. These tropical oils, as they are called, can be avoided totally without too much problem - but you do have to read the labels on everything. It is very important to avoid them, though.

It is also advisable to avoid the over-use of sugar, alcohol, and stimulants.

Now that we have looked at the "avoids," let's look at some of the "includes" in a heart-healthy diet. Vitamin C reduces the risk of heart disease by reducing the risk of blood clots. Beta-carotene is also an antioxidant helpful in reducing heart risks.

Some common foods that are good sources of vitamin C include: broccoli (it's best to eat it raw or microwaved or stir fried, not boiled), bell peppers, cabbage, parsley, strawberries, sweet potatoes.

Common foods that are high in the beneficial beta-carotene include: broccoli (best to eat it raw, microwaved, or stir fried), cabbage, carrots (it's best to eat them cooked because your body can more easily assimilate the beta-carotene), sweet potatoes.

Common foods that fight cholesterol levels and cholesterol build-up in the arteries include: apples, carrots, cooked dried beans, oat bran, rice bran, strawberries, soy protein, water packed tuna, raw white or yellow onions. Grapefruit pectin is also effective in combatting high blood-cholesterol.

Eating only a few foods in large amounts and eliminating everything else could do more harm than good. Try to eat a well-balanced diet that is relatively low in saturated fats and cholesterol and get plenty of exercise. If you need them, take vitamins and dietary supplements. Maintaining a healthy body is a good way to reduce heart attack risks.

One vitamin supplement that actually reduces cholesterol levels and improves your circulation is NIACIN. Taken in large doses (about 1500 mg) each day, it can reduce your cholesterol level. DO NOT take that much at first. Take smaller doses to begin with. If you are not accustomed to taking niacin, it can cause some discomfort. It is not harmful but can be very uncomfortable. It will make you very hot all over your body and you may turn a bright red or look like you are breaking out with a rash. This does not last long but is uncomfortable. You should begin by taking smaller amounts for a while and work your way up to larger doses. This is a supplement your doctor may not tell you about. It is used by some doctors for their heart patients or patients with an existing cholesterol problem, but most doctors use prescription medications for these patients. Niacin is much cheaper than the prescription medications and has lowers side effects. Few doctors will mention niacin to patients who are not experiencing cholesterol or circulation problems. Niacin can be purchased without a prescription.

It is important to keep your weight moderate. Going on and off a diet, bouncing up and down the scale register, has recently been found to be very bad. Don't go on crash diets. Eat a healthy diet to keep excess weight off. A low fat/limited sugar diet keeps your cholesterol and tri-glyceride levels down as well as helping to keep your weight down.

Exercise is important. The best exercise for your heart is walking. There are many benefits to be gained from walking briskly with arms moving. You should walk at least a mile a day, but work up to it gradually. To be beneficial your walk should be continuous. You should not stop at a friend's house for coffee halfway. Walking a couple of blocks several times a day is not the same as walking a mile all in one stretch. But, like we said, work up to it . Don't attempt long distances if you are not accustomed to exercise. And remember, when you walk away from your house, don't keep walking until you are exhausted — you have to walk back home again.

Walking burns calories so it helps to keep your weight down. It also speeds up your heart so it gets some exercise. Your heart is a muscle, and it benefits from the work it has to do like your other muscles benefit from exercise. It becomes stronger. Walking also lowers your cholesterol level. And, finally, it relaxes and calms you. It reduces stress.

Reducing stress is important in reducing your risk of heart attack. It's not easy to reduce the level of stress in your life in this world, but it can be done. Walking, as we mentioned, is a good way, but there are other techniques, too. You might find that sitting down, leaning back, and concentrating on something calm and pleasant will relax you. Or lean forward and let your head and arms hang loose while you concentrate on calm and pleasant thoughts. You could do this several times a day - even at the office. You might try meditating with or without the use of the "mood tapes" that are available in many stores. Or you might try some other exercise such as swimming. Whatever works to relax you will help to reduce stress. Just remember, it has to relax your mind and body. You need to get your mind off your personal problems, work problems, world problems, anything that you worry about. It must also be non-competitive. You should not even be competing with yourself. For instance, if you choose to walk to relieve stress, don't try to do a mile faster than you did the mile last week. Just walk briskly and let your mind go out to the beauty of the sky, trees, buildings, whatever is pleasant and unstressful to you.

Look at things in a positive manner. This is probably the most difficult part of a healthy heart program. It may take some time to get on track. Don't be discouraged. You can do it. Your walking will be the first step of your positive living program. Walking helps to relax you. But don't stop there. Some simple stretching and deep breathing several times a day will also help to relax you. When you are relaxed and more fit you will feel more positive about life. Train yourself to enjoy what you have even if it isn't all you would like. Few of us have everything we want. Focus on what you do have, not on what you don't have.

To achieve a positive attitude, you must also work on your relationships. Don't try to change or control the people around you. Learn to accept other people for what they are. The change has to be in you. Learn to open up, share your feelings, communicate. Join a support group that encourages sharing feelings. If you're not accustomed to sharing feelings, it takes a bit of work, practice, and encouragement to accomplish it. A group is very helpful in this. Or enlist the help of friends or family - make them aware of what you are trying to accomplish.

Often those people who are most prone to heart attack are people who set up artificial deadlines and tough goals for themselves. They create more stress in their lives than necessary. If you find that you are one of these people try to limit the artificial stress you create. Ask yourself if these deadlines are necessary. Ask yourself if the goals you set can't be relaxed a bit. Make sure the goals you set are attainable. Give yourself more breathing room. Give yourself some time to just relax and enjoy life. You might even find that you actually accomplish more when you are relaxed and under less stress.

So it all boils down to a simple program that isn't too difficult to abide by. As you begin to moderate your lifestyle you will find there are many immediate benefits as well as the long-term benefit of lower risk of heart attack.

The program in simple form is:

(1) Don't smoke and limit your alcohol consumption.

(2) Eat a healthy low-fat, low-cholesterol diet.

(3) Go for a brisk but not stressful walk every day.

(4) Maintain a moderate weight - between your healthy diet and your daily walking this should occur without much extra effort.

(5) Practice positive living. This includes relaxation and learning to communicate and share your feelings - reducing the stress in your life.

Eating a healthy diet, exercising, and reducing the stress in your life will reduce your risk of heart attacks. These are all relatively easy techniques that will make you feel better now as well as give long term benefits.

The 10-Point Proven Sleep Program

How much sleep does a person need to function properly? Well, it depends on the person. Some people feel just fine with only four hours of sleep per night. Other can still feel groggy after eight complete hours. It seems that Mother Nature has put each human being together differently. So don't feel guilty if you find that you have to stay in bed for eight to ten hours. That doesn't mean you are lazy or "slow." It just means your body needs 10 hours rest on most nights to function properly. Some of the greatest minds of our centuries can be found in either category. If Albert Einstein didn't get 10 hours per night he felt "fuzzy" all day. Another genius, Thomas Edison, could get by with just two or three hours per 24-hour period.

The moral of this story is that you as an individual must do a bit of experimenting to find out what is best for you. You may have been taught that eight hours is the optimum for all people, but that's just not true. If you feel like you are too tired during the day, maybe you should increase your sleep time by an hour. Go to bed earlier. If that doesn't work, try an hour more. On the other hand, you could be forcing yourself to get too much sleep. That can be just as bad! Find the hour amount that is right for you and then stick with it.

What about insomnia? How much sleep should you be missing to qualify you as a bona fide insomniac? Well, it's not the amount of sleep you get — it's getting enough that's right for you according to your individual needs. Generally, a person has insomnia if his or her ability to sleep interferes chronically with daytime functioning.

Whatever the cause of your problems with sleep, the following proven 10-point program will help you get the proper amount of rest that is right for you.

(1) Sleep as much as you need to feel refreshed and healthy during the following day, but no more or no less. Cutting down on sleep time slightly can lead to better, deeper sleep. trying to sleep too long, on the other hand, can result if fragmented or shallow sleep.

(2) Getting up at the same time every morning can strengthen your cicadian cycling and will help you fall asleep at a regular time each night. A cicadian cycle is basically a 24-hour biological rhythm. Fine tuning that rhythm can solve all of your sleep problems.

(3) You may not be getting enough physical exercise during the day. Even if you are mentally exhausted from a day at the office, your body may still have some energy it wants to expend. If that's the case, your body may not want to go to sleep. Try a half hour or more of exercise every day after work, if you have a desk job. You won't believe how beneficial this will be to your sleep. On the other hand, never exercise right before bed. That will ruin your sleep! Do it in the late afternoon or early evening.

(4) If you have frequent noise near where you sleep, it may be having a profound effect on the quality of your sleep even if you never awaken. Noises such as loud trucks, aircraft, loud neighbors, etc., can make sleep more shallow and less restive. Take measures to soundproof your room. Move if you have to. But make sure you don't have to listen to noise even in the unconscious state of sleep.

(5) Many people believe that having the room temperature just a bit cooler than normal waking time temperatures will improve sleep. But this is not what is found in extensive sleep lab tests. Extreme temperatures of either hot or cold, however, will definitely disrupt sleep, so keep temps even and regular.

(6) If you are hungry, you may not be able to get to sleep. Many people do not like to eat before they go to bed because they think it will cause bad dreams, or make the digestive system work too hard while you are trying to sleep. There is little or no truth to either tale. A heavy meal before bed is not recommended, but a light snack (especially one which includes warm milk) will help you get to sleep.

(7) What about sleeping pills? A very bad idea! There are many problems associated with sleeping pills — serious problems — so you should avoid them at all costs. One of the first problems that arises with sleeping pills is addiction. Certainly, a powerful sleeping pill will conk you out nicely, but when the next night rolls around, you will be heavily tempted to pop another pill ... and then another, and another. Before you know it, you'll never get to sleep again without a drug. Sleeping pills will also interfere with your sleep. That may prevent you from dreaming properly. The end result will be less wakefulness the next day and you'll soon be worse off than you were with insomnia. While an occasional sleeping pill may be a quick fix, they are never a good idea for long.

(8) You already know this, but it bears repeating. you must avoid caffeine, especially after 5 p.m. Even people who can drink a lot of caffeine during the day with no apparent nervousness or "buzz" could be affecting their sleep more than they realize. Heavy caffeine users may have more shallow sleep. Caffeine is a drug, after all, and it can prevent your brain from going as deep as it needs to in the sleep process. Knocking off caffeine entirely is never a bad idea, although difficult to do. Like most drugs, caffeine is addictive, and there are few positive addictions.

(9) A lot of people think that alcohol is a good sleep aid, but nothing could be further from the truth. Alcohol may allow you to sleep for a brief period, but you'll likely wake up soon after and then feel jittery. Alcohol ruins sleep after you do get to sleep, and it actually prevents you from sleeping all night. Avoid it.

(10) Don't try too hard to get to sleep! After about 20 minutes of sleeplessness, you will likely be better off by getting up to read a book, listen to music or some other mild activity. Turning on the TV is not a good idea because it will stimulate your brain with too much noise and color, and that's not a very good sleep aid.

But even if you can't fall asleep, you should try not too worry about it too much. That will create a vicious circle of more insomnia. The more you worry and fret, the less able you will be to fall asleep.

The Breathing Method

Keeping in mind the information presented in the 10-Point plan we have just presented to you, there is another way in which you can easily beat insomnia without drugs or complex behavior modifications.

You've heard of the old wives tale that counting sheep is a good way to fall asleep. Well, we don't know about sheep, but we do know that counting your breaths is a tremendous aid in getting you to drift away into blissful rest.

Perhaps one of the most common causes of insomnia is a mind that races at bedtime. You lay down, but your mind chatters on endlessly about your day's events, your problems and plans and just about anything else.

But you can get control of your mind by giving yourself this simple task: Tell yourself that you will think of nothing else but the breaths going in and out of your body. Also, you will count your breaths up to four times, and then start over. Count one inhale and one exhale as a complete breaths. When you have completed four breaths, start over at one again. You must be firm in your resolve to think of nothing but the counting.

At first it will be quite difficult, but throw yourself into the task. Even if you are not terribly successful about keeping your attention focused on the counting, you will be amazed at how many times this process will put you fast to sleep. Most of you will probably not get through more than three or four cycles before you drift off.

Some Essential Sleep Nutrients

Many sleep disorders are associated with a lack of certain vitamins and minerals in your diet. Taking a daily multi-vitamin may be all you need to ensure you are getting all the nutritional elements needed for proper sleep.

Two mineral supplements you should pay extra attention to are copper and iron. Not having enough of these two can actually disrupt your sleep process.

Iron

Good sources of iron? — almonds and raisins. Munching on some almonds with a glass of warm milk before bedtime may very well put you to sleep where you sit!

Copper

An excellent source of copper? — Clams! Yes, clams. But swallowing a few slimy clams may not be your idea of an excellent nighttime snack. Other good sources of copper are apricots, whole wheat pasta and Grape Nuts cereal. In fact, a bowl of Grape Nuts with warm milk, with a few iron-rich raisins added in for good measure, would be a superb sleep aid!

Smoking -- Dealing With the Demon Weed

You know that smoking is bad for your health. It is impossible to ignore that fact since the media and society tell us every day. It can contribute to heart disease, lung disease, and cancer.

In addition, society is turning smokers into pariahs. People are no longer allowed to smoke in most public buildings. And more places are going "smoke-free" every day. Many people don't allow smoking in their homes. It is beginning to seem that there is no place to smoke except outdoors. Even when you go outdoors, people often look at you with open disgust or make gestures and remarks to indicate their displeasure. Yes, smokers are becoming the pariahs of society.

Yet with all these inconveniences and embarrassments, do you find you are still smoking? Do you want to quit but find you can't? For many people, the habit has grown into an addiction and it seems impossible to quit.

If you really want to quit, there are some very effective aids and tricks to help you overcome the addiction.

First it will be of help to understand the problem. The habit, of course, is the physical act of lighting, holding, and smoking a cigarette. After using cigarettes for a time we develop little social tricks and habits using cigarettes. The habits come on gradually and naturally, so we not even be aware of them.

Examine closely your cigarette habits. Do you light up to make it past little hurdles and little discomforts in social situations? Do you reach for a cigarette when you feel bored? How about when tension has built up to the point where you feel a need to reduce excess energy?

Before you attempt to quit you should spend a few days asking yourself, "Why did I light this cigarette?" Ask the question each time you light up. Don't be flip with yourself. Examine your reasons closely and answer the questions honestly. Once you've discovered the reasons, the habitual lighting up will be easier to conquer.

If you find, for instance, that at times you use smoking as a social crutch, in effect you are probably "hiding" behind the cigarette or the smoke. Or maybe you are using the act of finding and lighting a cigarette to cover a pause in the conversation or to give yourself time to think.

Once you find the reasons and face them squarely, you can substitute some other physical act. Develop little social "tricks" to replace the cigarette as a social crutch.

If, as we mentioned, you hide behind the cigarette or smoke, then perhaps adjusting your glasses or passing your hand over your face will be a good substitute. While you use these physical tricks, tell yourself, "I can handle this little hurdle. There is no reason to feel threatened. I will not injure my health over a little social discomfort. It's not worth it."

Or if you are lighting up to cover a pause in conversation or to give yourself time to think, use the pause for an opportunity to look around. Or strike a thoughtful pose, or just say, "Let me think for a moment."

If boredom is the reason you are lighting a cigarette, you need to examine the reasons for the boredom. Are you bored when watching TV or driving the car? At what times of the day and under what circumstances do you find yourself bored and lighting up?

If TV is boring you to smoking, turn it off and substitute some type of physical activity - go for a walk, bake a cake, wash the car, call a friend, play with the kids. Or consider taking up a hobby that interests you and involves either physical activity or detail work that will keep you absorbed. If you are bored to smoking while driving, turn on the radio or pop in a good tape and sing along.

If you are using cigarettes as a way to reduce tension and excess energy, substitute physical activity. If the time and place permit, shoot some baskets, go for a swim, or jog around the block. If such vigorous activity is impossible at the time, just take a walk down the hall, stand up and stretch, or swing your arms. Just moving about a bit helps. Getting a drink of water also helps. In fact, we often light up when we are thirsty.

For each habitual reason that you light up a cigarette, there are acceptable, reasonable substitutes that you can develop. But it is necessary to examine your reasons and BE TRUTHFUL to yourself, even if the reasons seem dumb (and some will undoubtedly seem dumb). You can only develop effective substitutes if you understand why and how you are using cigarettes.

It's a good idea to mentally talk to yourself and encourage yourself as you develop substitutions. Your habits developed over a long period of time, and it will take time and self-encouragement to develop substitutions that will replace them naturally and - should we say it? - habitually. Yes, that's true! You will be replacing your habits with other habits. But the new habits will not be damaging to your health. Developing new habits is done more easily than you probably think. Humans are creatures of habit. An old saying but a truth. It is part of the reason you are smoking, and using that truth will make breaking the cigarette habit easier for you.

By now you are probably saying that this seems pretty simplistic and sometimes you just need a cigarette - it isn't habit, it's addiction.

Well, you are half right. For most of us it is BOTH a habit and an addiction. So, breaking habits is just half the battle. You have to conquer the addiction, as well.

The nicotine gums that are on the market (by prescription only) are one way of battling the addiction. The gum actually is a method of putting nicotine into your system without smoking. It gives you an opportunity to continue feeding the addiction while you work on breaking the habits of smoking. Then you taper off the gum. This can be quite effective, since you can split the problem in half and work on half at a time.

This is also the way "the patch" works. The patch, too, provides your system with nicotine - feeds your addiction while you do battle with your habits. The patch is available only by prescription. Sometimes a patch will cause an allergic reaction, but there are several brands available. If you break out from one, ask your doctor to prescribe a different brand.

There are other methods of battling the addiction. Maybe you want to quit on your own, without consulting a doctor. You must still work on both the habit and the addiction.

The real craving for a cigarette, the physical need, is the addiction - and it is physical. Since it is physical, sometimes just wanting to quit, knowing you should, and changing your habits through substitution are not enough - you still have the craving. Why? Because there are ingredients in the cigarette that your body has become accustomed to. And not just the nicotine - also sugar or a sweetness.

Have you noticed that many people gain weight when trying to quit smoking? There are two reasons for this: (1) They have not examined and controlled the habit side of the problem. Since they have not consciously sought acceptable substitutes for the habits, they have unconsciously substituted eating and nibbling. (2) Cigarettes contain a bit of sugar or sweetness so when they try to quit they crave sweets. Then when they eat and snack as an unconscious habit substitute, naturally they often choose candy and other sweet items.

Knowing that you will crave that sweetness when you attempt to quit, you can prepare yourself. Carry a small container of sugar with you. When you experience a craving for a cigarette, wet your finger and dip it into the sugar. Then rub it onto the inner side of your lips. This will help curb your craving! It will also help you to maintain your weight while you are battling your addiction.

Plain old chewing gum - not the nicotine gum - can also provide you with a bit of sweetness to curb the craving for sweets. The tiny mints that you can buy at most grocery stores can help, too. Neither of these has many calories so you shouldn't have to worry too much about gaining weight from them.

Find a support group to help you through the battle. Or find one or two people who either are quitting or have recently quit. No one can quit for you - you have to do the job yourself - but you don't have to do it alone. Having understanding and supportive people to talk to will make it easier. A cheering section always adds encouragement and raises a flagging spirit.

Remember you are battling both habit and addiction. You must work on both. Take it a day at a time. Steel yourself in the morning. Once you make it past the hurdle of the morning cigarette (try drinking a large glass of water as soon as you get out of bed) you will be encouraged to make it through the rest of the day. Once you make it past the first day, you will be encouraged to make it past the next. Each smoke-free day will feel like a major accomplishment, AND IT IS! Look at it as such. As you begin to pile up smoke-free days, you will not want to spoil your fantastic record. But, if you falter and smoke one, don't let it discourage you - renew your efforts. When you've been smoke-free for two weeks, you'll notice a difference in how you feel. That's when your job will become easier. You will feel better and breathe easier. Now is the time to tell yourself, "I feel so much better, I can breath easier. Food tastes better. I've done it! Now I'll continue it!"

But, remember, you are like an alcoholic - you must not allow yourself even one cigarette because you are vulnerable. You have quit, but you'll be on shaky ground for a while. You may not feel a great need for cigarettes now but smoking one may put you back to square one. The biggest hurdle is the first two weeks. Don't spoil it now!

Sexuality
Non-orgasmic Women

When a woman has difficulty achieving orgasm, it is not merely her problem. It is also her partner's problem. So they must work together to solve it.

Sometimes the problem is physical. Some of the physical problems that affect a woman's ability to reach orgasm are: aging, imbalances of hormones, injury or inflammation, over-indulgence in drugs or drink, or inborn defects of the sexual system.

Sometimes the problem is psychological. These problems can include stress, guilt, fear, shame, depression, resentment of her partner, fear of pregnancy, or just being too eager to succeed at achieving an orgasm and thus too tense to do so.

But many women can eventually reach orgasm, EVEN IF THEY NEVER HAVE BEFORE, if she and her partner are patient and work together.

The solution will not come overnight. It will take time and patience. It will take many sessions of working (or rather playing) together. This does not have to be frustrating. Indeed, it MUST NOT be frustrating or you won't succeed in solving the problem. You must decide before you begin that you will have fun.

If you follow the steps listed as a guide for fun and pleasure — with fun and pleasure in mind — you'll enjoy the process and set yourselves up for eventual success. I use the word success here to refer to achieving orgasm eventually, but each session that you enjoy and find pleasure in is a success EVEN IF THE SESSION DOESN'T CULMINATE IN ORGASM OR EVEN INTERCOURSE. Pleasure is the only success you should be striving for — let the rest happen naturally.

This guide is not meant to be followed through to the end in one session. Perhaps your first session will be spent only caressing the upper body for an hour or so. That's OK. Only go as far as is comfortable. Don't rush! If it takes ten or twenty sessions to get to actual penis insertion, that's OK , too. Whatever you are comfortable with. Just enjoy. Sex sessions without intercourse are fun and build anticipation.

Just remember, the woman must not feel rushed or pressured to have intercourse and achieve orgasm. If she is to eventually become orgasmic, she must feel unthreatened and in control for now. She must have the opportunity to explore and discover the pleasure the man can give her through her body. It will be an adventure for the man, as well. He will have the opportunity to learn from her what he can do to increase the pleasure he gives her. This is a fun and pleasurable learning experience for both of you. Remember, pleasure is the only objective for now.

Find a comfortable, private place where the woman feels secure and need not fear interruption. Plan to give yourselves plenty of time so you don't feel rushed. Unplug the phone.

Patience is very important. The woman must feel relaxed and unpressured. For those reasons, orgasm and even intercourse should NOT be the objective of your sex play for a time. If it leads to that - fine, but it is important to just focus on pleasure and fun until the woman does feel relaxed and ready for more. If that means several sessions of sex play without actual intercourse, her partner must be willing to cheerfully comply with that, and LET HER CALL THE SHOTS for now.

OK. Ready for the fun and games?

First, as we said, the woman must be relaxed. The time and place must be comfortable and private. The man should lightly caress her while tenderly telling her how much he loves her, how special she is. This he must do with patience and no rush. There should be an understanding that this need not lead to intercourse but is merely for pleasure. Together you should explore and find the areas she most likes having caressed.

The man must be careful to be gentle, considerate, loving, and patient. The woman should be allowed to guide his caresses, especially in the inner thigh, vaginal, and clitoral regions. She needs to be able to control her sensations so they do not become too intense for her.

Do spend a lot of time at this. Several sessions - explore, explore, explore. Talk to each other. The woman must let the man know what she likes and also what she really doesn't like. The man should encourage her to share these feelings. He should not take offense and get angry if she doesn't like being touched in some places or in some ways that he thinks she should like. Each person's body is different. Each woman differs in the kind of lovemaking she likes just as men differ in their likes. This is a mutual discovery session and neither of you should feel insulted if the other does not like something that is tried. Keep it light, keep it fun, keep it loving, and keep it relaxed!

For some couples, reading and looking at erotic books and magazines or talking about sexually stimulating topics may help. The man must be gentle and considerate and not accusative, condemning, or demanding. He must tell her she gives him pleasure and how much he loves her.

For other couples, perhaps masturbation by hand or use of a vibrator or oral-genital contact will bring her to orgasm. Once a woman achieves orgasm by one means, it will be easier for her to reach orgasm by other means.

When the woman feels safe and comfortable, she should try penis insertion from a position with her on top and in control. The man must be guided by her. If she wants to just remain still, he must remain still. She should direct all movement to her pleasure and desire. It should be understood that pleasure - not orgasm - is the objective. The man should show her the pleasure he gives her and tell her how much he loves her.

Once she is comfortable with this position and feels a sense of controlled pleasure, you are ready for the position that is most conducive to female orgasm. This need not be during the same session of sex play in which the woman takes a position on top. In fact, it is most likely that the preceding activities will take place over several quiet, relaxed, and loving sessions. You may want to have several sessions with the woman taking top position.

The use of the ultimate position should not imply that orgasm is the objective. Pleasure should still be the primary concern. She should not feel pressured in any way. The man must continue to be gentle and understanding and keep telling her how much he loves her and how much pleasure she gives him.

The position the couple should assume is lying sideways facing one another. She will place her lower arm under his neck and her other arm under his upper arm and around to his back. He will place his lower leg under her near her waist and curl it down past her buttocks for added support. She will place her upper leg over his thigh, bend it slightly, and rest her foot on or just behind his knee. In this position she will be resting mainly on her chest, stomach, and waist. She will have less control of her hip movements. Spontaneous hip movements will be less restricted making orgasm more likely.

It is necessary to focus on sensuality and pleasure rather than position and orgasm. Until the position feels comfortable and natural, not artificial, orgasm is unlikely. Practice the position for pleasure until it becomes comfortable.

When the position becomes comfortable and pleasurable and the woman feels secured, loved, and unpressured, she will be more likely to achieve orgasm.

Not every woman is able to achieve orgasm even after these sessions and using this position. But even without orgasm, sexual play and intercourse can be fun and pleasurable. These sessions will help both of you relax and enjoy sex more fully.

Other female sex problems

If your libido (sex drive), desire, sexual pleasure, and orgasm ability seem inhibited or non-existent, ask your doctor about bupropion hydrochloride, an antidepressant. Although most antidepressants have an adverse effect on sexual performance, bupropion has positive effects. It tends to increase a woman's desire and assertiveness. It can even bring about orgasmic ability in non-orgasmic women.

As a woman ages, vaginal tissues can become dry. This creates discomfort, but can be easily remedied with an over-the-counter sexual lubricant. Or ask your doctor to prescribe a lubricant containing estrogen - a cream that will heal the tissues while it relieves the dryness.

Menopause is a decline in bodily production of hormones. You may also experience a decline in libido (sex drive). Increasing the declining estrogen level in your body can increase your sexual pleasure. Ask your doctor about estrogen. It can be taken by mouth, patch, injection, or vaginal cream. If estrogen is not effective, ask your doctor about methyltestosterone, another hormone.

More On Sex

Improving a Man's Sexual Performance

Is your sex life something less than Fourth-of-July rockets and flares? Are you longing for a few more firecrackers? Do you think advancing age is playing a not-so-funny trick on you? Or are you worried that there is something seriously wrong with you or your relationship?

Well, if it's just the firecrackers seem to be missing, you and your relationship are probably OK. You can easily bring in some fireworks if you want to.

First, let's take inventory of the situation. Look at your life-style. If you are like most people, you are "living on the run," so to speak. You are probably stressed out most of the time and tired the rest of the time. Although it's true that a good sex life can reduce the stress in your life, it is also true that stress works like a cold bucket of water - it can make the fireworks sputter and fizzle. You may need to cool down your life a bit so you aren't so stressed.

Or maybe you need to break out of a rut and try lovemaking at a different time of the day, preferably when you aren't so tired. After all there is no rule that says you MUST make love ONLY at night when you are both ready to conk out after the pressures of the day.

As long as we are challenging the "rut syndrome," we may as well look at other changes that can add some zip to your sex life. Has sex developed into a routine? Try something different - a different location, for instance. You don't have to make love in the bed - or even in the bedroom, for that matter. Do it in the shower, or make it a romantic interlude in front of the fireplace. Stir up something in the kitchen, or do it in the van. Different is exciting. That goes for position, too. There are 101 different positions, but you've probably settled into a routine of one or two. Why not try others? You'd be surprised how much a change can spice up your love life.

Communicate with your partner. Talk about sex. Talk about what each of you likes. Buy a sex manual, read it together, and talk about it. Get into the habit of whispering to your partner during your lovemaking. Let each other know when you like a caress. Let each other know what you are feeling.

Bring lovemaking into the rest of your relationship as well. A simple wink or pat or squeeze of a hand during the day can communicate your love for one another even in a crowd - or in front of the children. Make your partner feel loved all of the time and your sexual relationship will be enhanced. Romance shouldn't have to be confined to the bedroom.

Read the section elsewhere in this book about building a happier marriage. You will find several secrets to a more satisfying sexual relationship. And hey! ... they're fun!

But what if the problem is not just missing fireworks? What if you have the desire but your body isn't up to the physical aspect of the performance?

Well, don't panic if an erection isn't happening every time you expect it to. Whether they admit it to each other or not, nearly every man has had this happen at one time or another. The most serious part of an occasional erection problem is your attitude about it. An occasional episode of inability to gain an erection can stem from several different things - tiredness, too much to drink, stress or drugs. If you worry about it a lot, and also about future performance, you are almost certain to intensify the problem.

Keep the problem in perspective. Your masculinity is NOT threatened, even if you feel like it is. The episode itself is not as important as how you react to it.

It is important to talk with your partner about it. She may not understand and may feel that her desirability has diminished in your eyes. Be open and honest about what has happened - talk about it - after all, you can't hide the fact that it has happened. A worried or

embarrassed silence will certainly not help anything and may
devastate your relationship.

Talk about how important your relationship is - how this occurrence
is not unusual - explain that nearly every man has this problem on
occasion. Talk about your feelings and ask how she feels about it.
Whatever she feels about the episode - and she may feel her
femininity is threatened - don't try to change how she feels. Trying
to change how she feels will add to your frustration. Just try to
understand how she feels.

But you also should talk about the things you can do to keep
impotence in check- and there ARE things you can and should do.

Let's start with a definition. A failure to achieve or maintain an
erection at least 25 percent of the time is called impotence. By
definition, then, premature ejaculation is also an impotency
problem. As you can see, an occasional inability to achieve or
maintain an erection is not classified as impotency. However, an
understanding of the causes and remedies for impotency can be of
help with the occasional problem, too.

Now, let's examine some of the causes impotency and some of the
things you can do to enjoy longer and better sex.

As we said before, tiredness can be a cause of problems. The
remedy? Get some rest. Consider taking a vacation. Don't try to
force your tired body to perform. Wait until you feel more rested.

Alcohol can be the problem. Even a couple of drinks can cause
problems. You may think alcohol improves your performance, but
even though it may increase your desire, it's a depressant and
decreases your performance. Continuous use of alcohol can cause
liver damage. This, in turn, creates an excess of female hormones
in your body. With an improper balance of hormones, you can
expect to have erection problems.

Is stress the culprit? Try to eliminate some of the stress from your
life. Taking a nice long walk every day can lessen stress. Try a
mile a day. While you are walking consciously relax - think about
the trees, sky, anything but your problems and heavy schedule.
Just the physical act of walking brings about physiological changes
in your body. But consciously turning your mind to pleasant things
is an added benefit.

Are you on drugs? Many recreational drugs, prescription drugs and over-the-counter drugs can cause problems. Avoid cocaine, heroin, marijuana, and other recreational drugs.   Blood pressure pills, tranquilizers, antidepressants, diuretics, heart medications, arthritis medications,   antihistamines   and   many   other   prescription medications   cause   impotence.   Over-the-counter   medical preparations that could be the cause are: antihistimines, diuretics, sedatives and others. If you are taking any drugs regularly, check with your doctor or pharmacist. If they feel your medications could be causing the problem, they may be able to decrease your dosage or change you to a different drug.   DO NOT ADJUST YOUR MEDICATION ON YOUR OWN.

Are you anxious about your performance?   This can create problems. Relax. If you are afraid of failure, your body may react by   producing   excessive   amounts   of   a   hormone   called norepinephrine causing an inability to achieve an erection. A good way to relax is to make an agreement with your partner to engage in sex play without worrying about whether it will end in intercourse. Just plan for a session of sensual fun and games. Not all sex play has to lead to intercourse.   Check out the section about non-orgasmic women elsewhere in this book. It lists some great ideas for fun and games.

Are you giving yourself enough time? As you get older, you may need a little more time. Men under 20 can achieve an erection almost instantaneously. If you are between 30 and 50, you may need a couple of minutes of genital stimulation. At 60, you may need longer. Relax. Give yourself plenty of time.

Your refraction period - the time from ejaculation until you can again achieve an erection - also increases with age. If you are over 60, your refraction time may be a day or more. Don't try to push your body beyond it's limit. An increased refraction time is not a sign of impotency.

Do you smoke? Nicotine is a blood vessel constrictor. Since penile erection depends on blood flow, the use of nicotine could cause problems. Consider quitting or at least cutting down the amount that you smoke.

Are you in pain? Your body reacts to pain by producing opiates.

This can cause an inability to achieve an erection. All you can do is wait until you are feeling better.

Do you consume caffeine? Coffee and soda pop often contain a great deal of caffeine - a stimulant. As we said before, you need to be relaxed - so switch to the decaffeinated variety of your favorite beverage.

Are you depressed? Depression can affect sexual performance. This is a touchy situation since most anti-depressants can increase sexual impotence. Bupropion hydrochloride, however, is an anti-depressant that increases sexual desire and functioning. If you are depressed or are now taking anti-depressants, ask your doctor about this drug.

Do you take potency enhancers? These are often stimulants. We repeat - it's important to be relaxed. Stimulants have the opposite effect. Don't take so-called potency enhancers containing stimulants.

Watch what you eat. Whatever affects the blood flow in your arteries also affects the blood flow to your penis. Erections depend upon blood flow. So, watch what you eat. Go on a low-cholesterol, low-fat, cardiac diet. A program for reducing your risk of heart attack will also benefit your sex life. Elsewhere in this book you will find a section on reducing your risk of heart attack. Read it carefully and, remember, whatever reduces your cholesterol will help you avoid impotence.

Take niacin, an over-the-counter vitamin. It helps to increase blood circulation which, as we said, is an important factor in ability to gain an erection. As an added benefit, it helps to reduce cholesterol. A great aid to longer and better sex!

Get exercise. Exercise is good for your circulation, reduces stress, and tones up your body. Toning up your body is important because you will feel better about your body. Feeling good about your body will make you feel more confident and sexy. But don't exercise too much - if you get carried away with exercising your body will produce opiates like it does when you are in pain. It will lessen your ability to achieve an erection.

Try an external vacuum devise. This is a devise to help you achieve an erection. It does not require drugs or surgery. It is merely a small hand held pump with a cylinder. You slip the cylinder over your penis sealing it against your body. When you pump, a vacuum is created drawing blood into the penis, and an erection is formed. You slip a latex ring onto the base of your penis before removing the cylinder - the erection is maintained by the ring. It only takes a couple of minutes and you are ready for intercourse. The devise is available by prescription.

Try an injection of prostaglandin E1, papaverine, or phentolamine. These drugs are effective for impotence and premature ejaculation. They stimulate the blood flow into your penis and produce an instant erection. Your erection can last from 10 minutes to two hours - it depends on the dosage - regardless of how many times you ejaculate.

Premature ejaculation can sometimes be controlled by a woman-on-the-top position, because muscle tenseness sometimes plays a role in the problem. When you are on the bottom, you can be more relaxed and be responsible for less of the movements.

Try therapy for premature ejaculation. The therapy is effective, easy, and quick - just a few weeks. No, it's not the extensive lay-on-the-couch-and-talk-about-your-childhood type of therapy. You are taught to know your body signals and how to control your ejaculations. Call your nearest sex therapy center. You may even be able to arrange for the therapy to done by phone.

A Beautiful Smile

A smile will light up your face - make you look younger, more confident, and friendlier. But you want it to be a bright smile. You want white, healthy teeth to show when flash that sexy grin.

Good dental care, of course, begins with regular brushing. When you brush, use a proper technique. Scrubbing back and forth is not good. Neither is brushing up and down. So what's left, how should you brush? Place your brush at the base of your teeth at your gum line. Gently wiggle the brush in small circles without lifting it from the teeth and without moving in a large area - confine the work to a couple of teeth at a time. This will loosen the plaque. After working on each tooth in this manner, brush by placing the brush at the base of your teeth and pulling it away from the gum. Then lift the brush, place it at the base again, and pull away from the gum again. You see the difference from brushing up and down? With this method you never brush toward your gum. Brushing toward the gum can lodge material between your gum and your tooth.

Use a small, soft bristled brush. It will work just as well to loosen plaque as a stiffer brush and will be gentler on your gums. A small brush works better to get at all sides of your teeth.

Or use an electric toothbrush. Be sure to get the kind with bristles that rotate. Use it similar to using a regular brush - confine your work to a couple of teeth at a time. These brushes are very effective when used properly and regularly.

After you have brushed, it is a good idea to use a water sprayer made for the purpose of cleaning your teeth. But don't depend on the sprayer alone! You do need to brush.

And don't forget to floss. This is very effective in controlling plaque. Floss gently and thoroughly. Like with the brushing, be sure you work in motions away from the gum - go upwards on your lower teeth and downward on your upper teeth.

To fight tooth stains: Brush after every meal. Make a toothpaste by mixing baking soda with a little hydrogen peroxide. Use a mouthwash with an anti-bacterial additive. Or make your own mouthwash mixing equal amounts of water and hydrogen peroxide.

Removing food particles immediately after eating will cut down on plaque build-up. If you can't brush after a meal, rinse your mouth with water. Be sure to swish it between your teeth. Or chew sugarless gum. It will loosen food particles from between your teeth. It also promotes your natural production of saliva, which helps to neutralize the acid in the plaque.

Eat about an ounce of aged cheese BEFORE a meal. It will eliminate the acid in the plaque and help prevent tooth decay.

Visit your dentist for a check-up at least once a year. Leave the use of abrasive stain removers to the dentist. You should not use abrasives at home. You could damage the enamel on your teeth, leaving them more susceptible to stains.

With regular, proper care you can flash that sexy grin with

confidence.

Your Personal Health Care Resources Guide

If you put together the vast resources of the U.S. Government and the dozens of private foundations which exist to provide free medical help to people, you will have a source of free health care information and services that is second to none in the world.

Yes, it's true that the American Health Care System is becoming a bigger more expensive nightmare everyday, but it's also true that by doing some homework and making the right phone calls, you can get the health care you need at a vastly reduced rate — or even free.

It's up to you to find what you need. But we are going to make your search for low-cost health care and health care information a lot easier. We have rolled up our sleeves and searched out dozens of phone numbers and addresses you can use to get free information on everything from how to find the best surgeon in your area to where you can get help paying your medical bills.

We hope the following sources of information lead you to the just what you need to lead a happier, healthier life — without going bankrupt in the process.

Five Thousand Sources of Free Health Care!

We want to start out with what we think is an excellent resource for millions of people out there who are in desperate need of low cost or free health care. By calling this toll-free number, you can locate 5000 clinics or hospitals that deliver free or low-cost medical care.

Call 1-800-492-0359 if you live anywhere in America, or 1-800-638-0742 if you live in Maryland. (Note: the toll-free number does not serve Hawaii or Alaska). For those of you who live in those states, write:

BHMORD-JRSA
5600 Fisher Lane
Rickville, MD 20857

The staff at the other end of this number and address will send you a list of the medical facilities in your area that are participants in the federal Hill-Burton Free Care Program. They will also send you guidelines to tell you if you qualify for free medical care under this program.

With a little luck, you may be able to find health services through the above organization that won't cost you a dime. Why not give it a call? The call is free and you might obtain several thousand dollars in free health care. Better yet, you could save your own life or the life of someone you love.

Health Care Resources from A to Z

The following is a wide sampling of addresses and toll-free phone numbers where you can find help on just about any medical concern anyone might have. Scan through these resources to find the medical issue that concerns you. If you don't find the specific topic that concerns you, don't overlook the number under the Health Information section, which will direct you to the resources you need no matter how obscure your medical concern.

Abortion

To find out where you can have an abortion performed call: Abortion Advice and Referral: 1-800-438-8039.

To find out more information about abortion, contact Abortion Information Service: 1-800-321-0575.

National Abortion Federation: 1-800-772-9100.

Aging

Administration on Aging
330 Independence Ave., S.W.
Washington, D.C. 20201
Phone: 202-245-0671

Comments: This agency will tell you everything you need to know about growing old and how to cope with it.

AIDS

Center for Disease Control
Office of Public Affairs
1600 Clifton Road, NE, Building 1
Room 2167
Atlanta, GA 30333

Comments: This agency heads the national effort to battle the disease of AIDS. They supervise numerous other agencies and projects. You can write or call them with your questions. You can also call the Acquired Immune Deficiency Syndrome Hotline (AIDS) at 1-800-342-2437.

Alcoholism

National Clearinghouse for Alcohol Information
P.O. Box 2345
Rockville, MD 20852
Phone: 301-468-2600

Comments: Is the one-stop place for all kinds of information on the disease of alcoholism.

Alzheimer's Disease

For information about Alzheimer's call the Alzheimer's Disease and Related Disorder Association toll-free: 1-800-621-0379.

Arthritis

Arthritis Information Clearinghouse
P.O. Box 9782
Arlington. VA 22209
Phone: 703-558-8250

Comments: Gathers, collects and disseminates all kinds of information on the arthritis and similar musculo-skeletal diseases. Is also a place where individuals and organizations can exchange information and interact in any way they please. Cooperates with the Arthritis Foundation.

Asthma

For help with this chronic breathing problem, contact: Asthma-Allergy Hotline: 1-800-558-1035.
You can also call toll-free the National Asthma Center: 1-800-222-5864.

Blindness

For information about services available to the blind, call: American Council of the Blind: 1-800-424-8666.

Library of Congress National Library Service for the Blind and Physically Handicapped: 1-800-424-8567.

Cancer

Cancer Information Clearinghouse
National Cancer Institute
805 15th St. NW Room 500
Washington, D.C. 20005
Phone: 202-496-4070

Comments: Coordinates cancer information between individuals, general public, researchers, patients and health care professionals.

Office of Cancer Communication
Public Inquiries Section
9000 Rockville Pike, Bld. 31
Room 10A18
Bethesda, MD 20205
Phone: 301-496-5583

Comments: This organization will answer all the questions you have about cancer and its treatment.

Here is a toll-free number you can call for Cancer Information: 1-800-422-6237.

Cancer Causing Products: To obtain a list of 250 trade-name products which contain cancer causing substances contact:

Clearinghouse for Occupational Safety
and Health Information
Center for Disease Control

4676 Columbia Parkway
Cincinnati, OH 45226
Phone: 513-684-8326

Another toll free number you can try for general information about cancer:
American Cancer Society Cancer Information: 1-800-525-3777.

Children

For problems with child abuse, contact:

National Center on Child Abuse and Neglect
P.O. Box 1182
Washington, D.C. 20013
Phone: 301-251-5157

Here are some toll-free numbers for problems associated with children:

Children's Defense Fund: 1-800-424-9602.

Childfind: 1-800-431-5005.

Child Help USA (Child Abuse Counseling) 1-800-422-4453.

For advice for the children and parents of runaways call toll-free: 1-800-621-4000.

Sudden Infant Death Syndrome: 1-703-528-8480.

For maternal and children's health, contact:

National Center for Education in Maternal and Child Health
3520 Prospect Street NW
Washington, D.C.
Phone: 202-625-8400

Runaway Hotline (Will pass message from child to parent) 1-800-231-6946.

Parents Anonymous Hotline (child abuse) 1-800-421-0353.

National Hotline for Missing Children: 1-800-843-5679.
Shriners Hospital Referral Line (They provide free care to children who need orthopedic and burn treatment). 1-800-237-5055.

Dental

National Institute for Dental Research
National Institute of Health
Bethesda, MD 20205

Comments: You can write to the above address for a free pamphlet entitled Good Teeth for You and Your Baby. You can also ask them any other questions you might have about dental care.

Diabetes

National Diabetes Information Clearinghouse
Box NDIC
Bethesda, MD 20205
Phone: 301-468-2162

Comments: All the information there is to know about diabetes can be found through this resource. Ask them for publications they can send you free of charge.

Drug Abuse

National Clearinghouse on Drug Abuse Information
P.O. Box 416
Kensington, MD 20795
Phone: 301-443-6500

Comments: Produces materials on drug abuse and prevention. Also collects existing materials and disseminates information around the country.

For a toll-free number on drug abuse among children, call: National Federation for Drug-Free Youth: 1-800-554-KIDS.

National Cocaine Hotline: 1-800-COCAINE.

Epilepsy

Call this toll-free number with your requests for information about epilepsy: Epilepsy Information Line: 1-800-426-0660.

Family Planning

National Clearinghouse for Planning Information
P.O. Box 12921
Arlington, VA 22209
Phone: 703-558-7923

This center gathers written materials on family planning. They have many publication for distribution to the general public. Call them and they'll find you a lot of useful information.

Handicapped

Clearinghouse on the Handicapped
330 C Street S.W.
Washington, D.C. 20202
Phone: 301-344-3719

If you are handicapped, or know someone who is, you can call this resource and they'll answer your questions and direct you to the help you seek.

Health Information

National Health Information Clearinghouse
P.O. Box 1133
Washington, D.C. 20013
Toll-free phone: 800-336-4797

If the individual numbers we have provided for you in this section do not help you, calling the National Health Information Clearinghouse may help lead you through the maze, no matter what your medical concern. The purpose of this organization is to help the general public find health care information.

Hearing

Call the National Hearing Aid Helpline: 1-800-521-5247.

Better Hearing Institute, toll-free 1-800-424-8576.

National Association for Hearing and Speech Action Line: 1-800-638-8255.

Heart

National Heart, Lung and Blood Institute
Public Inquiries and Reports Branch
National Institute of Health
Building 31, Room 5A-52
9000 Rockville Pike,
Bethesda, MD 20205
Phone: 301-496-4236

Cardio-Care Testing, toll-free number: 1-800-822-4826.

If you have a pacemaker or if your doctor is recommending one, call: International Association of Pacemaker Patients: 1-800-241-6993.

High Blood Pressure

High Blood Pressure Information Center
1501 National Institute of Health
Bethesda, MD 20205
Phone: 301-496-1809

Comments: Provides information to the public about how to control and lower high blood pressure.

Injuries

National Injuries Information Clearinghouse
5401 Westbard Ave. Room 625
Washington, D.C. 20207
Phone: 301-492-6462

Comments: This organization deals primarily with injuries that people suffer as the result of consumer products. They will refer your questions of a general nature to the Consumer Products Safety Commission.
Kidney Disease

Call the American Kidney Fund, toll-free: 1-800-638-8299.

Mental Health

National Institute of Mental Health
5600 Fishers Lane
Rockville, MD 20857
Phone: 301-443-4513

Comments: All the literature you could want on mental health problems of all kinds. Has many free publications available.

For more free mental health care information try calling toll-free: The American Association of Mental Deficiency: 1-800-424-3088.

National Down Syndrome Society Hotline: 1-800-221-4602.

National Institute of Mental Health: 1-301-443-4513. (Not toll free).

Parkinson's Disease

National Parkinson's Disease Foundation: 1-800-344-7211.

Poisoning

Office of Epidemiology and Biostatistics
Food and Drug Administration
Room 15B-23, HSN 730
5600 Fishers Lane
Rockville, MD 20857
Phone: 301-443-6260

Comments: This agency has a real intimidating name, but basically it can be helpful to you because they can direct your emergency calls to a local poison control center.

Pregnancy

National Pregnancy Hotline: 1-800-344-7211.

Pregnancy Crisis Center: 1-800-368-3336.

Rape and Sexual Abuse

National Center for the Prevention
and Control of Rape
5600 Fishers Lane, Room 6C 12
Rockville, MD 20857
Phone: 301-442-1910

Comments: This organization maintains a list of rape prevention
and treatment resources to help people locate services available in
their local area.

Rehabilitation

National Rehabilitation Information Center
Catholic University of America
4407 8th St. NE
Washington, D.C. 20017
Phone: 202-635-5822

Comments: A central location for all publications and videos that
have to do with rehabilitation. These folks will also answer your
questions and direct you to resources you need. You need not be a
Catholic to use this resource.

Sexual Diseases

The National Institute of Allergy
and Infectious Diseases
Bldg. 31 Room 7A32
Bethesda, MD 20205

Comments: Provides information on all aspects of sexually
transmitted diseases Write to them for a free booklet on sexually
transmitted diseases.

Or call this toll-free number: Venereal Disease Hotline: 1-800-227-
8922.

Skin

National Tetinitis Pigmentosa Foundation: 1-800-638-2300.

Smoking

Office on Smoking and Health
Park Building, Room 110
Fishers Lane
Rockville, MD 20857
Phone: 301-443-1575

Comments: Mostly for people who are involved in research, or who are searching for professional information. But you can call them for help and information that may lead you to a way to solve your problem with smoking.

Speech

National Center for Stuttering: 1-800-221-2483.

Spina Bifida Information and Referral: 1-800-621-3141.

Surgery

National Second Surgical Opinion Program
Health Care Financing
Administrative Office of Public Affairs
330 Independence Ave. SW
Washington, DC 20201
Phone: 202-245-6183
Toll-free number: 1-800-639-6833
1-800-492-6603

Comments: If you doctor has recommended non-emergency surgery, this is a must call number. You should always get a second opinion before undergoing any non-emergency surgical procedure. By calling the toll-free number listed above, you will find help in finding a surgeon or specialist who can assist you in your decision about having surgery. When you call, ask for the publication: Thinking About Having Surgery.

Some Miscellaneous Resources of Interest

American Medical Radio News: 1-800-621-8094.

Medical Scholarships from Health Services Corps: 1-800-638-1824.

National Gay Task Force Crisisline: 1-800-221-7044.
Organ Donors Hotline: 1-800-24-DONOR.

The Living Bank (for organ transplants): 1-800-528-2971.

Women's Sport Foundation: 1-800-227-3988.

If you've been turned away ...

If you have been denied treatment at a health care facility because you are on Medicare/Medicaid or low-income assistance call Hill-Burton Hospitals toll-free: 1-800-638-0742. The folks at Hill-Burton have resources in nearly all parts of the United States that can assist people who have no credit or financial stability find health care regardless of the their financial status.

Life Style Section
Living Up To Your Potential

If you want to make more of your talents - live up to your full potential - you have to learn to use them. You have the power to change your habits - to acquire new skills and fully use the skills you now have. You can improve your performance, your productivity, and the quality of your whole life.

What makes a high achiever? Is it luck, intelligence, talent, dedication? All of these things figure in - they all make a difference. But we all know intelligent, talented, hard-working people who do not consider themselves very successful or even happy. And we know people who are not exceptionally bright but seem happy and successful.

So there must be something else, some secret to success. Actually there are several secrets to achieving your peak performance - living up to your full potential.

Your success at business, friendship, love, sports - just about anything you try - is largely determined by your own self-image.

Your unhappiness is something you choose. So, you're thinking no one chooses to be unhappy. Well, maybe not - but you have to consciously choose to be happy, self-confident, and successful.

Happiness is elusive when we go after it directly. So is self-confidence. Both seem to be more "side-products" than something you can achieve in and for itself. So how, then, can consciously choosing to be these things be of any value? Well, the secret is to focus on other things.

First, focus on your potential. Begin by making a complete and accurate assessment of your potential. To do this you must take an inventory of yourself - you will make a few lists. Sit down and make a list of all the things you can do well. Be honest with yourself. When that list is done, make a list of all the things you like to do, even if you think you can't do them well. Then, make a list of all the things you would like to do, if you could. Now list your hobbies.

Then, go back to the list of things you can do well. You are probably being much too hard on yourself. Most of us are. We have this little voice in our heads telling us things like: "You're so dumb," or "You can't learn to do that," or "You never do anything right," or similar nasty things. And even worse, we listen to that voice as if it's telling us the gospel truth. So now, shut off that voice - you can do it - and add a few more things to the list of things you can do well. Pretend you are your best friend - it's amazing how much more forgiving and charitable we are with our friends than we are with ourselves. Now that you are your best friend, you should be able to add a few more items to your "do well" list. But do be honest - don't list things you feel you really can't do well.

Next, go to your list of things you like to do but you feel you don't do well. Speaking as your own best friend, do you think there are some things on this list that could be moved to your "do well" list? There probably are. If you like to do it, chances are you do pretty well at it. Treat your hobby list in the same manner.

Next, go to your list of things you would like to do if you could. Ask yourself, "Why can't I do this, if I'd like to?" Put your reasons on another list. OK. So you have a lot of lists going - what good is that going to do? Well, you have just made an assessment of yourself. If you have been truly honest in making these lists, it may even be a fairly accurate assessment. Probably it isn't, but that's OK. This assessment isn't carved in stone. It's subject to change. But for now we will work with what's on the lists. At least you have a place to start.

Look over your lists again. You are focusing on all the things you feel you can't do and the reasons why you can't do them, right? Well, don't. FOCUS ON WHAT YOU CAN DO - FOCUS ON YOUR POTENTIAL. Make it a habit to focus on your strengths. Don't forget to include your undeveloped potential, as well. Train yourself to focus on your potential instead of your limitations.

Now that's not to say that you should ignore your list of reasons for not doing some of the things you would like to do. Not at all! But look at them from the viewpoint of your strengths. For instance, you'd like to play basketball but you think you are too short, so you don't even try. In this case, you are looking at it from the viewpoint of your limitations. Now, when you look at it from the viewpoint of your strengths, you would say, "Well, I may be pretty short to play, BUT I am fast. I can handle the ball well. I have a lot of stamina. I can't change being short, but I can refuse to let my limitations overcome my strengths."

You see the difference? Focusing on your limitations lets those limitations make your decisions for you. Focusing on your strengths lets YOU make the decision. To go back to our example: when you've decided to overcome your height limitations to play basketball - something you really want to do - you will be more determined to develop your strengths to compensate. You will do well, because you will be doing what you really want to do and you will be determined to develop the full potential of your strengths. Very few people concentrate on fully developing any of their strengths. That's where you will have the edge. You know your true disadvantages but your determination, your singleness of purpose, will inspire you to fully develop the talents and skills you do have.

OK. You probably have no interest in playing basketball. Then go to your assessment of yourself. What do you have a major interest in? What do you have a natural aptitude for? Go for it. Devote yourself to something you really like to do. Don't choose something just because you think you could make more money at it than you could by doing something else that you would really rather work at. You won't work to develop your full potential. You may start out with enthusiasm, but you will soon flag. It will be a chore to go to work. You'll probably find yourself hating to go. It'll be difficult to work on improving your skills because you don't like what you are doing. You probably won't be working up to your potential. Your success will probably be limited by your growing lack of interest and your happiness will surely be affected.

If, however, you devote yourself to something you really like to do, you'll enjoy your work, you'll be enthusiastic, and you'll probably find yourself working on improving your skills just for the sheer joy of it. You will be working to reach your full potential. You'll probably soon find you are making more money at this truly interesting occupation than you ever dreamed possible. And because you like what you are doing, you will be happier.

When you know you are working to your full potential and you enjoy your work and begin to feel successful, you will find that self-confidence and happiness soon follow.

But, you must be realistic and honest with yourself. If you set goals that you can't possibly reach, you are setting yourself up for failure. You will make yourself frustrated and unhappy. The key here is a realistic and honest assessment of your potential.

Although most people will be unnecessarily harsh in their assessments, it is easy to become too hopeful when you start breaking down barriers. If, for instance, you're extremely interested in and fond of music and would love to be a singer, it would be unreasonable to set a singing career as your goal if you can't sing a note (some talents are inborn). But if you are knowledgeable about the music business and would be happy being involved in some other capacity, then it would be reasonable to pursue a career in the business.

Be wary of making otherwise perfectly reasonable goals unattainable because of stringent time frames. When you set a goal, you will most likely set times for achieving certain steps along your way to achieving your final goal. Even if you don't set the time frames formally, you will probably have a pretty good idea of how long you are giving yourself. It's wise to sit down and formally set these goals. Think about it and give yourself reasonable time to achieve them. Make a deal with yourself to view these time limits as flexible.

Don't get discouraged if things don't work out as planned. Sometimes finding our place takes both time and error. All of us experience failures of one magnitude or another. The key is to view the failures as a learning experience - if nothing else, failures teach us what not to do. Remain flexible. As long as you keep focusing on your strengths and potential, the right thing will come along - and probably sooner rather than later. But don't quit at the first sign of boredom. Even if you have truly found your niche, you will not feel enthusiastic 100 percent of the time.

Don't worry about others - don't compare your progress with that of others. No matter how successful you are, there will be someone else who, to you, looks like she's got it made - who looks like she's getting where you want to go faster and easier than you are. Maybe she is. Maybe she isn't. Who cares? Focus on your own achievements. Work to develop your skills and talents to their full potential. Compete with yourself - your short term goals should be based on today's accomplishments. If you have reached Point A today, make Point B your next objective - improve yourself and don't worry about the other guy.

OK. You have decided what your ultimate goal is. Make sure it is a definitely defined goal. "Someday I want to be famous" just won't cut it. Define exactly what you want to do. Define a reasonable time frame. Know what you have to do to get there. You don't need to know every little detail, but you do have to have the big picture and many of the details. If you have a goal in mind but don't know what it takes to reach it, then you need to find out. Do some reading, talk to people who know, ask questions and LISTEN to the answers. Think that sounds like a lot of work? Well, remember what you are preparing for - your success and happiness. Surely you want to put a little effort into that! Anyway, a little research into what it will take for you to reach your goals isn't too difficult.

Train yourself into making this "research" the next focus of your life. You will be focusing on your strengths, on your purpose, and on learning and doing. If you have chosen a goal that is right for you, focusing on these things and devoting the necessary time should not be too difficult. It may take a bit of self-discipline at first, but your determination and interest will carry you through until the focusing process becomes a habit. When you have a real desire to accomplish something, initiative should only require an occasional shove - but you may need to give it a nudge now and again.

Get into the habit of visualizing your success. Now sitting around and daydreaming in generalizations about it is not what we mean. You need to visualize specifics. To return to the basketball example, daydreaming about being carried off the court on your teammates' shoulders is just daydreaming. Picturing in your mind how you will work a play if your opponent makes a particular move, picturing your exact response to it, is visualizing specifics. If you run through specific moves in your mind, you will be prepared when the need for those moves arises.

Don't be afraid to use your imagination to visualize new and better ways to accomplish things, as well. Here in your mind, you can try doing things in ways that are different from the usual. This is a creative process - you may have heard of creative thinking. Training yourself to think creatively is largely learning to let your imagination work on methods that are different from the "way things have always been done." It's breaking away from the idea that a thing can be done effectively in only one way. It's looking at a problem from all angles. Just play a game of "what if." Ask yourself, "What if I did this thing this way?" It's OK to get a little crazy sometimes. But, you must also spend some of your thinking time at specific visualizations of the moves you need to make to accomplish your goals.

Visualizations are important but actual physical practice of your skills is important, too. Practice the boring little skills that are necessary as well as the skills that you enjoy. Don't let yourself rely on just the things that come naturally and easy to you. Develop your limited potentials as well as those that you feel are your assets.

Work on developing the more general attributes that are important to almost any goal:

Success comes more easily to those who have a pleasing personality. This is not to say that you should bend to everyone's wishes or scrape and bow. Rather, develop an attitude that is respectful of other's opinions but true to your own beliefs. Be flexible - don't be so rigid that you can't accept another's opinion when it is superior to your own. Be willing, even eager, to learn from others. Changing your opinion in light of more facts is a sign of strength of character, not weakness. Be willing to extend a helpful hand, be a team player. Develop a sense of humor. Be polite and caring - but be your own person.

Learn to guard against emotional responses. You are susceptible to errors of judgement when you let your emotions get in the way. Of course, everything we do is done based somewhat on our emotions, but strong emotions have little place in decision making. Hold your emotions in check. Try to delay decisions if you are in an emotional state. Learn to ignore your emotions and use reasoning to arrive at your decisions.

Develop the habit of enthusiasm. Enthusiasm works like a magnet - it draws people and success. It's a pleasing personality trait that people like to be a part of. It seems to be contagious - the people around you become enthusiastic, too, and become more cooperative. Enthusiasm sparks initiative and singleness of purpose.

We've talked of working to develop habits - the habit of focusing on your goals, the habit of focusing on your strengths, the habit of learning and "researching," the habit of visualizing, the habit of enthusiasm. Now we will talk of habits in a little different light - breaking them. First, assess your habits looking for the ones that may be displeasing to others. Offensive habits can hold you back from success - they are often a part of an unpleasant personality. Look for things like grumbling or grunting at people instead of answering, gazing at anything but the speaker when conversing, smirking or sneering when you don't agree - anything that is an automatic, displeasing mannerism. It will be very difficult to assess your habits accurately. After all, a habit is something that we do without thinking much about it. You will have to spend some time at this and be very conscious of yourself. Ask someone you trust to help you with this assessment. It may take a lot of work to break yourself of displeasing habits. Try substituting a different, more pleasing behavior for the habit you wish to break.

OK. You have set definite goals, you have a definiteness of purpose, you have researched and know the specific steps to take to achieve the goals, you have resolved to be flexible and to develop a more pleasing personality. Now what?

Well, just because you have a clear purpose, know what you want, are willing to work on developing your potential, and willing to be a nice person, success will not drop into your lap overnight.

You will probably find that one of your first steps in achieving your goals will be to take a job somewhat below where you hope eventually to be. But you've already analyzed the steps to your goal, so you presumably have planned for this. However, you do want to advance and, of course, as quickly as possible.

As you advance toward your goals, you will undoubtedly run up against some difficult people (maybe even difficult bosses), and there will be times you'll need to deal effectively with them. Since you are working on becoming a nice, enthusiastic person and a team player, you already have half the battle won. Your attitude is as important as the other guy's attitude when you are dealing with difficult people.

Always keep in mind that your job is a training field for you. You are getting paid as you learn the things you need to know to achieve your goals. Pretty good deal, right? If you view your job as a paid opportunity to advance toward your goals, you will be an asset to your boss. You will also be a happier, more productive person. Viewing your job in this manner will allow you to view the difficult people you will inevitably need to deal with as an opportunity to grow. From them and the situations they create, you will learn to negotiate with, side-step around, and draw out the best in others without letting yourself become upset. Each time you successfully deal with one of these people you will gain confidence and probably friends to add to your support network. The skill of negotiating with difficult people and the confidence you have gained from these encounters comes in handy when you are ready to ask for a promotion or raise - even if your boss happens to be a nice person.

Successful negotiation is not a contest of wills - it is working together to solve a problem or come to an agreement. It is an opportunity to learn how others feel about the issue.

Always be prepared. Know who you are talking with. Always know as much as possible about the person. Know about the person's marital status, family, hobbies, education, difficulties, attitudes, and whatever else you can learn. The information may give you an understanding of the person. If you know the circumstances, you will more easily find the most effective way to get your point across.

At the very least, the information will make the person seem more familiar which will give you more self-confidence.

Know the issue - not just your opinions about it. Be able to back up your opinions with reasons and research. If you are asking for a promotion, know the demands of the job in question. Know and be honest about how much of the job you are already qualified to do and how much additional training you will need. If you may not be as qualified as someone else applying, be prepared to negotiate for a smaller-than-offered salary until you are fully trained - remember the training is worth a lot to you. Be enthusiastic and focus on your strengths - don't boast but give an a simple and accurate listing of the strengths you feel make you a good candidate for this job. The strengths you cite can and should include specific job related skills, your present accomplishments on the job, your interest in the field (not just this job), your enthusiasm, your ability to work as a team member, and other personal traits that will be an asset on the job.

Always enter into negotiations with a calm and reasonable manner. Don't let emotion and emotional outbursts have a place at the negotiating table. You must be in control of yourself if you want to get your point across. People are more likely to listen to your views if you present them in a calm and reasonable manner. Present your ideas with conviction but don't try to intimidate others or be demanding. State your views simply, completely, and orderly. When you are expressing an opinion rather than a fact, use a qualifying "I think" or "In my opinion." When others are expressing their views, listen carefully and ask questions if something isn't clear. Don't disagree until you are sure you understand their position. When you do disagree, do so in a pleasant non-threatening way. "I see what you mean, but . . ." or "I can understand why you think that, but . . ." are a couple of good ways to begin a statement of disagreement. Be courteous and leave them a chance to save face.

Be prepared to face people who are not calm and reasonable. Don't let them get to you. Remain calm and reasonable and even be a little sympathetic. Let's say you have entered into negotiations with your boss for a raise and he blows up with, "I can't afford to give you a raise. This business isn't exactly a gold mine. Don't you realize how tough times are?" Remain calm. Put yourself in his shoes. Try to find something you can agree and sympathize with. For instance, look sympathetic and agree, "I know you have a lot of expenses and you work hard to keep this business going. It must be really difficult for you sometimes." This will probably not be the response he expects. It will probably take the wind out of his sails. Most likely he will calm down, and since you are sympathetic to his problems, he'll be more willing to listen to you. If you remain calm, reasonable, and sympathetic, he will calm down. When he is more calm, discuss with him the reasons you are a valuable asset to him. Don't threaten but calmly and reasonably discuss the bargain a small raise is. With that small raise, he'll be keeping a happy and fully trained employee who knows the company. When you consider the expense of finding and training another individual, giving you a raise is a bargain for your boss.

Play "Let's Make A Deal." Be prepared to deal. Don't expect to get everything you want. If you are willing to gracefully make some concessions, you will be more likely to arrive at a satisfactory deal. After all, a negotiation has at least two opposing sides. This means someone else has something they want, too - even if that something is simply to leave things as they are. Arrive at a compromise that everyone can live with. Remember, you are working at long-range goals, and you may be negotiating with them again.

Developing your potential more fully is a key to happiness and fulfillment. Although we have primarily discussed this in terms of a job, these same concepts can be used in many other areas of your life.

In developing your potential to it's fullest, you will want to become a more efficient person - get more done in less time - so you can take full advantage of the opportunities that you make for yourself. You will note that most effective, successful people seem to accomplish a great deal. It's true that this is partly due to enthusiasm, but there's more to it.

The first barrier to efficiency is procrastination - putting off getting started. Sometimes you know you are procrastinating. You may not want to do the task at hand so you keep putting it off until tomorrow. The thing to do is to look at it from a different angle. If it'll have to be done sometime, tell yourself, "why not do it now, and get it off your back." And that's just where it is! On your back dragging you down. Putting things off makes everything harder to do. If you keep putting things off, you'll soon have several things piling up, and then the sheer number of tasks you have backed up will make it seem impossible to ever get caught up. This affects everything you do try to do.

Sometimes you don't even realize you are putting things off. You may keep yourself extremely busy doing things of little importance to unconsciously give yourself excuses for doing the things you really should be doing. You say to yourself, "Look how busy I am. I just can't get everything done." But the result is the same as when you know you are procrastinating. It soon bogs you down. All you are doing is "running in place."

So how do you beat procrastination?

The first step in beating procrastination is to admit to yourself how often you do it and assessing your methods of doing it. Not very difficult, really, when you become aware of the tactics some of us use to hide from ourselves what we are doing.

The key in overcoming procrastination and becoming more efficient is organization. Plan ahead. Know what you want to accomplish today, this week, and in the long haul.

Make lists. The lists for today will probably be more detailed than the longer-term lists. That's OK. Now look over the lists and rank the tasks in order of importance. Make three or four groupings based on importance. Within each group, star the things you least like to do.

Each day you will have a "today" list to work on. Tackle the tasks that are most important first. If you have several "most important" tasks on your list, take on the least liked things in that grouping before you do the better liked ones. When you have accomplished a task, check it off. You'll be surprised what a good feeling you have when you check things off. What a sense of accomplishment! It's an incentive to do the next task on the list. When you have completed the tasks in the first grouping, begin on the list of next importance. Again do the starred items in that group first. Keep on checking things off as you get them done.

Do you see what is happening? You get the most pressing, least liked tasks out of the way early in the day when you are fresh and rested. As the day goes on you will feel less and less pressure. You have reserved the less important tasks for the end of the day when you will be more tired.

With this system you will have not only increased your efficiency but also reduced some of the stress in your day. Stress can get in the way of efficiency. Your new efficiency will help you develop your potential. It is, in fact, a part of living up to your potential.

Another important part of efficiency is in delegating work. If you are in a position where you have assistants or designated people under your supervision, you need to learn to delegate. If you are not in such a position yet, you still need to know - since you're working on developing your potential you very likely will be some day.

Delegating work is difficult for many people. Some find it hard to ask others to do things for them - others find it hard not to demand that others do tasks. Delegating is an art.

First, you need to realize that the people under your supervision are PEOPLE. Seldom, if ever, should you demand - that takes away self respect. In order to achieve a happy and co-operative crew, you need to help them build self-respect and self-confidence. A happy and co-operative crew is an asset to you. Demands do not promote self-respect and co-operation. Oh, it's probably effective to demand in the short run - but in the long run you will be better off to gain co-operation without demanding.

People who are asked to do a task, are given explanations and clear instructions, and are praised for a job well done will grow in self-respect. They will also respect you as a good supervisor. If you hesitate to ask for their assistance, your crew will feel that you do not trust them or have faith in their abilities. This affects their self-respect and, as a reaction, will affect their respect for you, as well.

When you delegate work, don't delegate just the "junk" tasks. Your crew needs to be given some important tasks to do as well as unimportant ones. The important task gives them a sense of the respect you have for them and the faith you have in their abilities. It's a good idea to save some "junk" tasks for yourself. Perhaps the most respected and effective boss is the one about whom the crew says, "She never gives us anything to do that she wouldn't do herself." Why? Because, by her actions the boss is saying that, though her position is above theirs, she is still just "plain people."

Delegation of tasks is important because you can gain in effectiveness and get more done if you properly supervise a crew. Don't feel embarrassed or hesitant about delegating work. If it helps you to shine, it helps your crew shine, too. A well-run, effective department is a credit to the whole team. With proper delegating, you can help your crew achieve their potential as well as achieving your own.

All of us have untapped potential - perhaps even areas of genius - that we have neglected to develop. Whether your concept of success has to do with business, love, friendship, sports, a combination of these or something else, more fully developing your potential will help you achieve your goals. If you can learn to assess your potential, set realistic goals, and go after those goals with determination, organization, and purpose, you will use your potential more fully, gain confidence, and be a happier and more successful person.

Marriage

A happy marriage.

Some couples just seem to have happier-than-average marriages. Why is that? Were they just "made for each other"? Maybe they are just lucky. Don't bet on it — more likely they know the secrets to making a marriage fun and happy.

The big secret is that ANY couple can use these methods to build a happier relationship. We won't talk about working at a marriage here. We have two reasons for that.

First, any relationship — not just marriage — can benefit from these secrets. Second, most of the secrets involve fun, not work, and we believe you shouldn't look at them as work.

They do involve focusing your attention on your marriage and your partner and not letting the partnership slide into a boring routine, but that's not work. After all, we rarely call the really fun and pleasant things in our lives work even if we put some effort into making them fun and pleasant.

First, let's look at how you and your partner communicate. Is it mostly just grunts and complaints? Do you refuse to listen and respond when you are watching tv or reading the paper? Do you reserve your attention and communication time for others?

Then this is a good starting point for perking up your relationship. Right. But if you haven't been communicating for a while, how do you begin now?

One good way to re-establish communication is to make a date for the weekend — just the two of you, no kids, friends, or relatives. It doesn't have to be fancy or expensive — just nice, comfortable, and private. Now, private can mean a busy crowded hotel, IF that's what you both like and you'll be alone together without friends and family to demand your attention. Or, if you both enjoy it, you could go camping instead of going to a hotel. Together you will decide where you'll go on this first date of your new relationship.

But just going somewhere and being alone together won't do the trick. Make it fun. Pretend you are just learning to know each other — which in truth you probably are if you haven't been communicating lately. Talk to each other and listen to each other — but no talk about kids, dental bills, mortgages, or the things about your partner that irritate you. Sure, even in a happy marriage these things need to be discussed, but not this weekend. Right now you are probably thinking, "what the heck will we talk about then?"

Well, remember this weekend is a date. Talk about fun, pleasant things. Tell each other jokes. Speculate about the strangers you see. Make it funny and laugh a lot. Share the fun and humorous things that have happened in your life, even from back when you were a child.

Or, get sentimental and reminisce about the warm, happy times you've shared: your first date, your wedding day, the births of your children, your first apartment, your first house, your first honeymoon.

Just remember, you are getting to know each other. Do not turn on the tv for the entire weekend. Make it your goal to laugh often and, as we all do early in a new courtship, be your best. Dress to impress your partner, behave to impress, and be sparkling and cheerful. You want your partner to have a good time!

Now, once the weekend is over, don't forget about it. You have a good start -keep it up! Keep talking and listening to each other and keep it light and fun. When you hear a good joke or something funny happens, remember to share it with your partner, Sharing humor gives your partner a chance to enjoy it and you an opportunity to laugh about it again. It also lets the two of you LAUGH TOGETHER and that's very important in a happy relationship.

Another thing to continue after your weekend together is dressing to impress. Well, right, you can't run around the house in formal wear all of the time, but you can be neat and clean. If you work at a dirty job, clean up when you get home. In the bedroom where no one sees you but your partner, don't wear "old rags." Wear nice attractive sleepwear, provocative and sexy things — or nothing at all, if that's what suits you.

But the main thing to continue after your weekend date is making some time for each other — alone. "Steal" some time for each other EVERY DAY. Make it a quality time for communicating — an uninterrupted time without tv or kids. Even if your busy schedule will allow only 15 minutes a day, do it. But give each other your undivided attention. Do it every day and talk and listen — nothing else, not even sex.

Well, no sex during your communication time, but sex really is a form of communication and is also extremely important to a happy marriage. In fact, another quick and easy way to perk up your marriage is by rejuvenating your sex life.

A good way to begin a "perk-up-your-sex-life project" is to learn to say "I love you" again — without sex. In many stale marriages, I love you is never uttered outside the sex act. Yes, I agree, that is one good time to say it, but people need to feel loved at other times, too. A little pat or hug and a whispered "I love you" at any time of day can cheer up both the receiver and giver. Daytime I-love-yous can make your partner feel really loved and appreciated.

Another neat way to say I love you is in a little note left where your partner will find it. Now, we aren't talking about the kind of note that says, "Don't forget to take the garbage out. P.S. I love you."

Those are OK, but a person could get hung up on the garbage and never really get to the I love you part. So sometimes, just try a little note that says, "You are special, and I love you" or just simply "I love you."

Learning to say "I love you" without sex is fun and really does help to rejuvenate your sex life. When you and your partner feel really loved and appreciated, sex becomes more fun.

Another way to spice up your sex life is to pretend you are having sex problems and set up several "discovery sessions" with a rule that the sessions cannot culminate in intercourse. Just explore and tell each other which caresses you like best. Relax and enjoy. You might like to follow the program for non-orgasmic women as described elsewhere in this book. After a few "discovery sessions," set up a special night for lovemaking.

Plan to meet at a hotel. It'll be more exciting if you arrive separately. Prepare for the evening — be rested, bring sexy nightwear — make it special. Have some wine or soft drinks and cheese and crackers available. Enjoy!

Or, pack the kids off to Grandma's and make it a special night at home — but devote the night to each other. Make sure there will be no interruptions and don't turn on the tv.

Buying a sex manual can perk up a marriage, too. If you page through it together, it can open up topics for discussion that neither of you dared to bring up before. It can give you an opportunity to find out how your partner feels about certain positions or acts you may be curious about. A manual can make you feel adventurous and encourage explorations that may add spice to your sex life.

Just as it is important to make time to communicate, it is important to make time for sex. With today's busy schedules, people often find it difficult to find a quiet private time for sex. By the time they are ready to settle down for the evening they are just too tired to enjoy sex. Make time. Send the kids to a babysitter for the evening or bring a sitter into your home and go to a motel. Try morning sex. This is a wonderful time for sex. You are rested and relaxed after a night's sleep. You will feel loved and happier all day. Be sure, though, to set your alarm plenty early to allow for a relaxed, unrushed time together.

Together time is very important to a happier marriage, but now we'll suggest just the opposite. You need some time apart, as well. It is good for a marriage if EACH partner spends some time on fun things with other people. Too much togetherness can make a marriage stale. The apart-time will give you a sense of freedom — you'll feel less tied down. It is important to tell your partner about your apart-time activities, share the fun and humorous things that happen. It is extremely important that EACH partner has some apart-time. If only one of you has apart-time, it will cause more problems in the marriage.

Some, but not all, of your apart-time might be used to visit your parents. Spend some time alone with them. It is good for you and good for your parents. It could be very good for your marriage, too, especially if your partner doesn't like the in-laws. It could mean your parents will get more attention with less strain on your marriage.

All marriages, even the really happy ones, suffer stress at times. During those times, you can declare a "Husband's Day," a "Wife's Day," or a "Consideration Week" to relieve the stress. A Husband's Day or Wife's Day is like a Mother's or Father's Day, only it doesn't involve the kids — just your spouse. It should be a day when you pamper your partner. Some suggestions: a gift, flowers, special dinner, night out, or a decorated cake -anything that shows your appreciation and love. Consideration Week is a full week of the same sort of considerate acts. The rule is that each partner must do at least one special thing for the other each day for a week.

Sometimes, though, even in the best relationships, you've just got to have a fight to let off steam. The trick at those times is to fight fair. This means, of course, no name calling. It also means to stick to the issue at hand. Don't dredge up things from the past. Don't personalize things. For instance, if you don't like the way your partner leaves laundry scattered in the bathroom, make it clear that he is OK and you still love him even though you hate the way he leaves his laundry on the floor. Attack the behavior, if you must, but don't attack the person. Keep an "I'm on your side" attitude: Some things you do bug me, but I'm on your side and I love you. Fair fighting doesn't threaten a relationship as much as dirty fighting and is more effective. Issues can often actually be resolved through fair fighting. After a fair fight, a relationship can settle back down more easily than after a dirty fight.

As you adopt new behavior techniques within your marriage, you'll be surprised at how much happier your marriage will become. You'll probably start thinking about renewing your vows and taking another honeymoon. Both are wonderful ideas! Renewing your vows does not have to be done formally. It can be done any time. For instance, sitting alone together and holding hands, you can re-dedicate yourselves to one another. Likewise, a honeymoon can be any time. In fact, we suggest one every year. It doesn't have to be elaborate or even very long, but it is important that it be called a honeymoon and without kids or friends tagging along. It's what you call it and the attitude about it that make it different from just a trip or a vacation.

In fact, what you call it and your attitude about it make a marriage what it is. If you both call it a happy marriage and shape your attitudes accordingly, you'll soon have a happy marriage.

Any relationship can improve with a little effort. When your primary relationship is happier, your whole life is brighter. It's worth a little effort— go for it!

JOBS

Forget the Want Ads and Find Your Dream Job!

If you are looking for a job, you probably know all too well about the daily frustration of scanning the Help Wanted ads in the daily newspapers. Finding a job through the Help Wanted ads rarely seems to work very well. Why? For the simple reason that hundreds of other people are also looking at the same ads and applying for the same jobs that you are. Even if you are well qualified, advertised jobs are likely to pull in dozens of other equally or better qualified people against whom you will have to compete.

By hunting for a job through the Help Wanted ads, you are working against the odds. But the fact is, there are hundreds of jobs available right now which have never been advertised, yet need to be filled. There are even jobs that have yet to be created — jobs you could create and then fill!

Why are some jobs not advertised? Well, in many professions, there is a lot of ongoing communication between the people who are already involved in that line of work. Everyone keeps in touch with what is going on within the industry. People get to now each other on and off the job and they exchange information by word of mouth. Each skill or profession — whether it be construction jobs or office work — has its own network made up of people who already have jobs within that network, or who have formerly held such positions.

Employers tend to hire from within the network. It's amazingly easy to keep tabs on what is happening in an entire state through word of mouth alone. So while many employers advertise for new employees, chances are much greater that they will hire someone who is already inside the network, or has once been an insider.

The question for you is: "How do I become and insider?"

There are several ways you can circumvent the Help Wanted ads and search out your own unadvertised job opportunity. We are going to show you three excellent ways to do this. They are (1) Personal Contacts (2) Direct Mail and (3) Placing Your Own Ad.

Personal Contacts

Millions of people find jobs every year through personal recommendations by people who know them. The people who can make a recommendation for you are former employers, business associates, your former teacher, clergyman, old college buddies, neighborhood contacts, bankers, merchants, friends, government officials or employees and many more.

You should make a list of every conceivable person who may have a line on a job for you, and then ask them to recommend you for a job interview. No matter who you are, you probably know someone who works for a certain firm, or knows someone who knows about a job opening somewhere. If you don't ask, you'll never find out.

If you are truly without a person whom can make a recommendation for you, there is a way to find some. You do this by writing an "advice letter." An advice letter is a letter you write to someone who you may or may not know asking them for their advice on who you might contact in your search for a job interview. Don't be afraid to write a letter to anyone, be it a top executive, or the foreman of a local landscaping crew. The worst they can do is let your letter go unanswered. But more likely, many will feel obligated to give you at least a lead or two.

Make your letter simple and straightforward. Brag yourself up just a bit and tell something about your qualification and your willingness to work hard. Then ask for a lead on a job. It's as simple as that.

Once you receive a recommendation, you should make sure you try "pyramiding" when you go to your interview. Pyramiding is simply asking the person who is interviewing you for additional leads within the industry. Be careful not to give your potential employer the idea that you are not interested in his business or in working for him, but you might as him if he can recommend others who are looking for employees as well. This will give the impression that you are really interested in going to work, and may make you look more valuable to the person who is interviewing you at the moment.

Yet another valuable place to make personal contacts for job recommendation is through social and civic clubs. Social or civic clubs are all about people coming together to cooperate and help each other toward specific ends. If you become a member of a club, you will have instantly developed dozens of contacts, many of whom may be able to give you leads or recommendations for job interviews.

We have touched on only a few of the possible sources of personal contacts for job opportunities. Using your imagination, you may be able to find dozens of sources of people who have leads on a job. The bottom line is that you have to always be on the lookout for people who have the kind of jobs that you want — and then you have to ask.

Direct Mail

Direct mail may be the most powerful ways to find the job that you want. By sending a letter about yourself directly to an employer you accomplish several things.

(1) You cut through the competition. While most people wait for an ad to come out and advertise a job opening, you can send a letter

that may find an employer before they even think about advertising. This will make you stand out and receive direct attention.

(2) In a direct letter you can project your best image and avoid disclosing your weak points.

(3) A direct letter puts the momentum in your court. By taking the initiative, you do a lot to set the tone and you can have more control over the subsequent job interview.

(4) With direct mail you can pick any employer you want in any field you feel you can qualify for. You can contact the top person in the place, and do an end-run around the lesser toadies who may filter your request out.

(5) Direct mail can uncover job opportunities which never existed before. If you make a good pitch in your letter, many firms will realize for the first time that they need a person like you.

People in top management positions know that finding and recruiting employees is expensive and time consuming. When someone good and ambitious comes to their attention without a whit of effort on their part, they will often appreciate it, and that can only be good for you.

Always try to send you letter to the top executive or head person at the place where you would like to work. You can send another letter to the personnel director, but it's more likely that a letter to that person will get filed with all the other resumes. You can also try contacting the Number 2 and 3 person in the organization.

10 Excellent Direct Letter Tips:

• Use the name of the boss or company president. Don't refer to him or her by title alone. Make it a tad more personal.

• Don't use bright or gaudy colored paper. It will not attract extra attention. Use plain white, ivory or off-white paper. It will make you look more down to earth.

• Put "private and confidential" on the outside of your envelope. That can work magic in getting you extra attention.

• Use the KISS method, that is, Keep It Short and Simple. Don't write a long-winded letter. Write in short, complete sentences and never go beyond one full page.

• Don't send out form letters. Each letter should be an original off your typewriter or computer printer.

• Never send a hand-written letter.

• Use a blue felt tip pen. As strange as this seems, a blue felt tip pen seems to improve response.

• Don't ask directly for a job. Just say you are looking for work and that you are well qualified, In short, don't beg.

• Be sure to state early in your letter that you have experience in the industry, or very similar experience. If you don't have experience, express great interest in the business.

• Research shows that January is the best time to mail direct letters to employers as you look for a jobs. June and July are the worst.

Advertising Yourself

You have probably seen those ads in the "Positions Wanted columns of daily newspapers. These are people who want to tell all potential employers that they are out there and ready to work. The only problem? The ads don't work! Extensive surveys of people who have placed Position Wanted ads have shown that almost 100 percent of them received zero or next to zero response.

So don't waste your money in the classifieds. If you want to advertise yourself, place an ad where it may appear unusual or out of place. Also, find the largest circulation publications you can find, and don't forget about major magazines. Newspapers are not the only game in town. Also place ads in newsletters, church bulletins and in other unusual places where they will stand out. The result is that you will stand out and people will literally come out of the wood work offering you jobs or leads.

You may also want to make up ads plugging yourself and posting them up on company bulletin boards, in community centers, churches, public buildings and on any busy street corner. Use a regular 8 1/2 by 11 sheet of paper. Make sure your name, qualifications, contact address and number are displayed prominently at the bottom of your ad. Don't stuff it too full of information. Remember, you can only make one point in an ad. Your point should be: "I want a job!" Then make sure people can find you easily and you will have the power of advertising working for your job search effort.

A College Education - The American Dream

A college education is the American dream - and it's becoming more and more of a necessity. In this "information age," a college degree talks. Better jobs are easier to come by if you have a degree. The climb up the promotions ladder is eased if you are a college graduate. You have more mobility in your career and are almost certain to command better pay and more respect with a college education. Yes, college is the American dream.

Most of us want our children to enjoy the benefits of a degree. Many of us who did not have the opportunity to get a degree when we were younger are yearning for it now. Some of us just see it as a personal need to satisfy within ourselves. Some of us see it as a way out of a rut or a dead-end job.

Do you or your children want to pursue that dream? You can - nearly anyone in this country who wants a college education can get one. So what's stopping you?

You don't think your child's (or your own) high-school grades are good enough? Well, that might pose a problem at some schools, but not all of them. Check out state colleges and community colleges. Some of these schools will accept anyone who has earned a high school diploma or a GED. These schools may not be as prestigious as others are, but they do offer a perfectly good college education. Often, these schools offer personal attention and assistance that you may not find in larger, more prestigious schools. They want you to do well and will help you achieve success if you are serious about it. And if you buckle down and prove you can earn decent grades, you can transfer to another institution - probably even that prestigious one.

So grades don't have to be a problem. But your age is? No way!

You can return to school at any age. In fact, some schools offer discounted tuition for senior citizens! Worried you'll feel uncomfortable because you are so much older than the traditional student? Surprise! In many college classrooms, 40 to 50 percent of the students are non-traditionals (a nice term that simply means older students).

OK. So now what's stopping you or your child from attending college? Oh, money? You think college is expensive? Right, it is. But don't let that stop you. You'd be amazed at how much you don't have to pay. That's right. You don't have to foot the entire bill yourself - in fact, you could get that education free or nearly free! But, most likely, no one will come knocking at your door to offer you a free college education - you will have to go looking for it. The first place to look is at the Federal Aid Programs.

The U.S. Department of Education sponsors several financial aid programs for students including:

(1) Federal Pell Grants
(2) Federal Supplemental Educational Opportunity Grants
(3) Federal Work-Study
(4) Federal Perkins Loans
(5) Federal Stafford Loans
(6) Federal Plus Loans
(7) Federal Direct Student Loans

Programs (1), (2), and (3) are grants - money to help you get an education and that you do not have to pay back. The remaining programs provide loans that must be paid back with interest. However, you use the money interest-free while you are in school (except for Federal Plus Loans). When you are no longer a student, the interest begins, but it is at a reasonable rate. The rate changes depending on the year that you are awarded the grant.

With the exception of the Federal Plus Loan, all of the aid from these programs (both grant and loan programs) is based on need. How do they determine your need and the amount of your financial aid? First, you have to fill out an application. The applications are free and should be available at high school. The college you plan to attend will have the application forms. You only need to fill out one application to be considered for all of these federal programs. Checking at your college for the form is a good idea because they have trained people who can help you with any questions you may have. They can give you advice on how to properly fill out the form.

Once you have filled out the application, the information you have given them is pumped into a formula and your expected family contribution is cranked out. This figure is used to determine your financial need. Basically, what they have done is determine how much they think you or your family can afford to pay based on your application. Then they subtract this amount from what they think your education will cost at the college you have chosen - including an allowance for housing, food, books, supplies, transportation, and child care. The cost of your education less the amount they think you can pay is your need.

How do they determine what you can pay? Well, it's a complicated procedure based on your income, your assets, how many students you have in your family, and other variables. It's about impossible to predict what the outcome of a particular application will be.

A couple of suggestions: (1) Don't try to second-guess the system. Even if you think your income is too high to qualify - APPLY. Very likely, you will be pleasantly surprised. (2) When the determination of your need has been made, you can appeal it. If the amount that they say you can pay is out of reach, go to the financial aid office at your school. Tell them it is out of reach and explain the circumstances that make it so. It's possible that an adjustment will be made. Don't demand an adjustment - they don't have to adjust it. Be honest about the circumstances and be polite and courteous.

Do you have to pay the amount that they determine you can contribute to your college expenses? Probably not. We'll discuss alternatives to that later.

OK. Now that they have decided what your financial need is, what happens? Well, based on your financial need your grant and loan eligibility is determined. Each of the programs is a little different.

Pell Grant:
The amount you get depends on your determined contribution, on what the average costs are at your school, on whether you are a full-time or part-time student, and other variables.

Federal Supplemental Educational Opportunity Grant:

The amount you get depends on your financial need and the availability of funds at your school. Your school is granted only a certain amount, and when that runs out, that's it for that academic term. You must apply early if you expect to take advantage of this program.

Federal Work-Study:
Like the grants, you don't have to pay this money back. Also like the grants you have to meet need qualifications before you can get work-study funds. But you do have to work for this money. You will be paid by the hour - graduate students may receive a salary. Your work hours will be assigned taking your class schedule into consideration - you won't have to worry about a conflict between class time and work hours. The hours you may work are limited. How this program is handled may vary from school to school. But you will probably have to ask about what kinds of jobs are available and then apply for any you want. The jobs probably won't seek you out even if you're determined to be eligible for the work-study program.

The Perkins, Stafford, Plus, and Direct Student Loans are different types of loans. Since they are loans, you will have to pay the money back if you take advantage of these programs. And you will have to pay interest on them. All but the Plus Loan defer the interest while you are in school. This means that you don't have interest accumulating while you are a student. All but the Plus Loan also defer payments while you are in school. This means you don't have to begin making payments until after you are through with school.

You will be notified of your loan eligibility at the same time that you are notified of your grant determination. You do NOT have to take the loans even if you do take the grants, Should you take advantage of the loans? Only if you need to - there are other sources of free money that we will look at later. But the loans are there to use if you need them so let's take a look at the Federal Loan Programs.

Federal Perkins Loan:
Perkins loans are for students with exceptional needs - those who have the lowest determined expected family contributions - those with the greatest need. Depending on your determined need, you can borrow up to $3000 for each year as an undergraduate and up

to $5000 for each year as a graduate student. You may be able to borrow more - the limits depend somewhat on your school. This is a loan and must be paid back after you are through with school.

Federal Stafford Loan:
Stafford loans are available to qualifying students who are enrolled at least half-time - you don't have to be full-time. The loan limits vary based on whether you are a dependent or independent student, whether you are a full-time or a part-time student, and on how much of your education you have completed. Independent students can borrow more than dependent students, and your loan limits raise for each year you have completed - you can borrow more when you are a junior than you could when you were a freshman. In general, the Stafford loan limits are greater than the Perkins loan limits. This is a loan and must be paid back after you are through with school.

Federal Plus Loans:
Plus loans are for parents of dependent students. The loan limit is the determined cost of your education less any federal grants you get. Plus loans are not deferred - that is, the parents must begin making payments while the child is still in school. Deferments are available for special circumstances - like loss of job or similar hardships.

Federal Direct Student Loan:
Direct student loans are basically the same as the Stafford and Plus Loans except that you will have a different lender - when it comes to payback time, you will pay the U.S. Department of Education instead of paying a bank.

If you decide to use the loan money, under certain circumstances the Department of Defense will repay a portion of your federal educational loans as an enlistment incentive. Check with your recruiter.

Other circumstances in your life can be an advantage in applying for federal aid.

For instance, income and asset information are important in determining your eligibility for financial aid:

If your child is dependent, then you must report your income and assets as well as your child's income and assets. If your child is independent, however, then your income and assets are not considered. You don't have to be a rocket scientist to see that a determination of independence, would be a definite advantage to the parents.

How is independence determined? You must be one of the following:
(1) Born before January 1, 1971 (for the 1994-95 academic year)
(2) Married
(3) A graduate or professional student
(4) Someone with legal dependents
(5) Orphan or ward of the court
(6) Veteran

If your child has been self-supporting, has not lived in your household for over a year, and has not been claimed on your last income tax filed, the student should ask the college financial aid officer for an independent status determination. It is possible that it will be granted.

Another important factor in determining financial aid eligibility is the number of students from your household. Perhaps you (or your spouse) have been planning to go back to school to get that degree. Now your child is about to enter college. If you both go at the same time, your eligibility for aid will increase. If you plan to go someday, now may be the time to do it. Some married couple decide to return to school together for the same reason.

OK. You've been awarded Federal Grant money and have been notified of you Federal Loan eligibility. Should you take advantage of it? By all means, if you need it. However, there is other free money available out there. Where?

Check your state grant and scholarship programs. Check for veteran's grants, if you are a veteran. Check for grants that apply to your field of study.

Check out private grants and scholarships. How? Check at the company you work for. Ask at your local high school. Ask at your college. Check with community clubs and organizations (especially if they have national affiliation). Look for minority programs that apply to you. Check out professional associations pertinent to your field of study. You might try a computerized scholarship search - but before you shell out money for a search, check out your high school, college, employment agency, charitable organizations that deal with crises, or your bank, or library to see if they have a free or minimum rate computerized search you can use.

Scholarships and private grants have less money over-all than state and federal grant programs. Some do, though, give much larger individual awards. Most require extensive applications.

Start a scholarship file and keep copies of every scholarship application you fill out. You will be able to use some of the information on them over and over. Soon filling out the applications will be much easier and faster because you have most of the information on file. Do be very neat and very accurate on the applications. Believe it. Even neatness is taken into consideration when the applications are judged. Answer each question honestly and directly. You can apply for as many scholarships as you want to apply for - there are literally thousands of them out there.

Some scholarships are very large and virtually provide you with a free ride through college. Others are small - one or two hundred dollars. Apply for any you feel you have chance at. The small ones can add up to a free ride. If you are awarded one or more small scholarships, don't stop looking. You can apply for and be awarded scholarships while you are attending college, too. In fact, some scholarships will only be awarded when you are a junior or have reached some other level of accomplishment. Be sure to read the guidelines for each scholarship before you apply. Don't waste your time applying for a nursing scholarship if you are not pursuing a nursing degree. The guidelines will be followed - the scholarship awards committee will throw out applications that don't meet the guidelines. But do apply if the guidelines fit. The competition is often stiff for some of the more popular scholarships, but many receive very few applications. Sometimes the ones you think would get a lot of applicants, get few. Go for it!

There are some very good sources for free education - totally free.

Check with your employer. Many companies will pick up the tab for evening classes. They want their people educated. Often they like to promote within the company, and if they provide you with free classes, they feel it benefits the company as well as benefitting you. Evening or daytime part-time education is just as good as full-time education and certainly better than not going at all. Eventually these classes can add up to a degree. It takes a lot longer, but if you are not going to school at all, you aren't progressing toward that degree at all. If you can do it for free, why not do it?

Also, check with your government job service office. They usually have some very good educational programs that will pay you to go to school. The circumstances that will qualify you for these programs vary, so check them out. If you are a displaced worker or otherwise unemployed, if you are on public assistance, if you are disabled, or if you are a single parent, chances are that there is some kind of educational assistance program available for you. If you are none of these, check it out anyway. You might find that there is some kind of program for you, too.

Yes, college is the American dream - let it become the American reality for you. You can do it and probably for a lot less money than you thought. All it takes is to start checking and start applying. With a little effort, time, and planning you can get that degree free or nearly free.

Improve Your Odds of Winning Sweepstakes

Have you been entering sweepstakes and contests and never winning? Do you feel the odds are impossible? Do you wonder if those advertised prizes are ever awarded?

Well, first of all the prizes REALLY ARE awarded. Sweepstakes and contests are subject to government regulations. If they are advertised, the prizes are awarded.

Now you are thinking, "But who wins them? I enter and enter and I never win a thing. The chances of my winning seem to be impossible."

Well, you are right, the odds are long in most sweepstakes. Your chances of winning are not very good. Is it worth your while, then, to enter the sweepstakes and contests? Well, you CAN easily improve your odds. And when you have won a large, wonderful prize, you will not be asking if it was worth your while entering that contest.

To become a true "sweepstaker" - one who wins - you have to channel your energies and postage money to purposeful use.

First, do not enter sweepstakes indiscriminately. In other words, choose with care the sweeps you enter. Look over the ads, subscribe to a contest newsletter, learn about the sweepstakes before you enter. If the prizes are not something you really want and you don't have the option of taking cash instead, save your postage and energies for a sweeps that offers a better prize. There are so many sweeps going on all of the time that you can pick and choose and still have plenty of them to enter at a given time.

When you have chosen the best ones for you, send multiple entries. You can afford to do this because you've saved postage on the sweepstakes that you decided not to enter. When you do send in those multiple entries, don't send them all on the same day. Send one every day or every couple of days or once a week right up to the closing date for entries.

For some sweeps, a few entries are randomly picked each day for the final drawing and the rest are trashed. If you have an entry arriving each day, you will have a better chance of getting into the final drawing. Even if a particular sweepstakes dumps the entries all together, your entries sent at regular intervals will be a "better mix" for the drawing, and your chances of being picked will be better.

You can also increase your odds of winning by entering local or regional sweepstakes instead of national ones. Sure, the prizes may be smaller, but your chances of winning are better because you are not competing against the entire nation for the prizes. Look at it this way, winning a smaller prize is better than losing out on a large one. And, those smaller prizes can soon add up to big winnings.

In local drawing-type sweepstakes, you can improve your odds by entering often and accordion pleating your entries. Simply fold your entries in one direction several times, press it with your fingers until the creases are crisp, and unfold it again. This will give your entry several points that pop up, making it more likely to be drawn.

The most important way to increase your odds of winning is so simple it seems foolish to mention it - Yet it is the reason many people never win. You MUST FOLLOW THE CONTEST RULES! Sweepstakes judges do disqualify entries that don't follow the rules EXACTLY.

If the rules state that you must enclose a proof-of-purchase or some printed words instead of that proof (called a qualifier), then you must enclose it. If the rules say use a 3x5 card, then you must use a card not a sheet of paper. And, it must be 3 inches by 5 inches. If the rules further state that the card must be unruled, then it must be unruled (have no lines). If the rules state that you cannot use a facsimile of the entry form, then you must use an official entry form. If they say use block letters, then you must print instead of writing in script. FOLLOW THE RULES EXACTLY even if they seem weird to you.

Note: When the rules require a proof-of-purchase or a qualifier, your chances will be just as good with the qualifier as they would be with an actual proof-of-purchase. But remember, make the qualifier EXACTLY as they tell you to. You will not win unless your entry meets the sweepstakes requirements exactly.

Technically, sweepstakes and contests are not the same thing. A contest is a competition where you must perform to win. You may be required to write a jingle or a poem. You may be required to answer a question or several questions. The idea is that you are required to do something special to enter, not just send in your name. These are technically contests rather than sweepstakes. Your odds of winning contests are generally better than for winning sweepstakes because fewer people take the time to enter them. Just remember, with contest, too, you must follow the rules exactly and that includes the rules for the qualifying performance (writing the jingle or answering the questions or whatever).

Yes, you can dramatically improve your odds of winning. Choose the best sweepstakes and contests, send multiple entries, and follow the rules exactly. Soon you'll be winning.

One last note: When you do win, send a letter of thanks to the sponsoring institution. That will increase the odds of more sweepstakes being sponsored by that company. Then you will have a chance to enter again.

Winning Big at the Casinos

What's more American than Mom, apple pie, and baseball? Would you believe Mom, apple pie, and casinos? It's true. Americans are visiting casinos more than they visit Major League baseball parks!

With all this participation, are Americans becoming expert at gambling? Do they know their odds and the ways to improve their odds the way they used to know baseball stats? If we are to judge by the billions of dollars dropped in casinos each year, the answer is a resounding "NO."

If winning at the casino is the new American dream, it seems to be a dream that comes true for very few - except the owners of the establishments. We'll assume you are not an owner. Then what can you do to improve your chances of winning a piece of the American casino pie? How can you change your luck?

Would you believe that your "luck" is really only one factor in the game, that there is a lot more going on here than just plain old-fashioned apple pie luck?

First, let me ask you a couple more questions. Do you spend more than you intended to on most of your visits to the casino, stay longer than you had planned, win far less money than you would like to win? Are you frustrated by your inability to really get ahead but find yourself going back again and again?

If you answered "yes" to these questions, you are solidly in with the vast majority of people who visit casinos. But, let's look at what "yes" answers imply. Notice that what you are really saying is that you don't seem to have as much control over your "luck" AND YOUR BEHAVIOR at casinos as you would like to have. Why?

Would you believe good old-fashioned American psychology? It's true - psychology is planned into the casino business!

First of all, there is the general psychology of society's changing attitude. Gambling has increased in popularity in good part because it is no longer perceived as terribly immoral - even the government has given its approval. Since you're, in effect, looking through society's view of gambling as an acceptable form of entertainment, it's easy to let your guard down. It's just an acceptable, harmless way to have some fun. This is fine, as long as you either have inexhaustible funds to throw away or you can keep enough control to spend no more than you can afford. But if you want to make your casino visits PAY, then you must change the way you look at gambling. To make it pay you must look at the casino as your adversary. Now, that's not to say it can't be fun - after all, wouldn't it be more fun to walk away from your casino-adversary with bucks in your pocket and a smile on your face than it is to walk away from your casino-friend with empty pockets?

But the psychology part is more involved and complicated than just analyzing your attitude and society's attitude. Casinos consciously and deliberately exploit known psychological responses to control your gambling behavior. Knowing some of their methods will help put you back in control.

We all know that casinos are set up to give the casino a mathematical edge. They are in the business to make money, after all. What you may not know is that your mathematical odds of winning are affected by the length of your visit. The longer you stay, the poorer your odds of winning are. That's mathematical.

The casinos, then, use psychological methods to persuade you to stay longer - the longer you stay, the greater the odds that they win.

The design of the casinos - the colors, the lighting, the space, the chairs, the smells in the air, everything - is analyzed for maximum comfort and appeal. The operators figure that anything that can keep you playing just another five minutes each visit can add millions to their take.

Let's take a critical look at some common casino practices.

Special promotions, for instance. Some are designed to get you into the place, others to keep you there just a little longer.

The free or cheap meals - an all around winner for the casino - will bring some people in for a bargain meal. How many will leave without dropping at least some money in the games? Most will end up paying dearly for that "cheap" meal, but will forget that the next time they want to go out for a nice, "cheap" meal. But there's another aspect to it. If you are already at the games, a cheap meal conveniently available in the casino will keep you in the building at mealtime. You'll be away from the games for a minimum length of time.

The fairly new bill acceptors on slot machines keep you at your play. When you are out of change, you don't have to wait around or walk to the change booth for more coins. This adds to your playing time - your playing time is money - for the casinos.

Casino operators carefully plan their lighting. You may have noticed that when you are in a casino it is difficult to determine whether it is day or night. This is deliberate. Remember, they like you (or your money) so much they want you to extend your visit. If they can get you to drop your usual time consciousness, you'll stay longer.

Colors are chosen to trigger automatic responses. Slot machines are outfitted in colors that will attract and hold gamblers. Sophisticated color combinations are used to minimize the time you will spend slot hopping.

Many casino operators add a scent to the air. Think that's silly? In an experimental test the scent was shown to increase substantially the number of coins customers dropped into the slots - very substantially, about 45 percent.

Most of these techniques add greatly to your comfort as well as sometimes triggering an automatic psychological response. If your visit is pleasant, you will stay longer, play looser with your bankroll, and come back again.

Other techniques have little or nothing to do with your comfort and are simply exploitive. You are simply the "white rat" - the unsuspecting victim of psychological games.

For instance, the payout system of the slots. In the last thirty years, psychology has even been applied to that. The system of paying tiny winnings often is that new. How was it done before? Well if you won, you won a reasonable amount, but the payoffs were infrequent. What is the advantage of frequent small payoffs? It is the psychological "promise" of a big win. You will be enticed into staying longer and risking more money.

Putting in a few "hot" machines is also an application of psychology. Your search for the "hot" machine is motivated by the psychological "promise" of a lucky streak. Again, you'll stay longer and risk more.

Some casinos will give you small denominations as change for large bills or, at the tables, small denominations of chips. The reason? Because, as we all know, it is easier to spend a dollar than it is to spend a twenty. Psychological? Of course.

Ever notice how wins are played up? The real coin that's dropped into metal slot pan when someone wins is deliberate. The noise excites you. The bells and whistles that attend a really big win are also deliberate attention-getters and exciting. The casinos make a big deal over wins - but losing is pretty quiet. The excitement of the noise stirs you to try to win. But there is more. All the attention given to winning makes it seem like there is more winning going on than there really is.

OK. Now you know that in the eyes of the casino you're merely a "white rat" from whom they are trying to extract the most they can. What can you do about it? Although occasionally casinos go too far and a practice is outlawed, you really can't do much about changing their use of tricks. But when you are aware of them, you can guard yourself against reacting automatically. You can put yourself back in control.

So, is being in control going to change your "luck"? Well, it will help. But you have to know how to use that control to your advantage.

First, you know that your odds of winning decrease in ratio to the length of your visit at the casino. So with your new control you will make your visits shorter. You will be aware of your surroundings and try to note the tricks the casino is using to influence you. Conscious awareness will make them less effective. Pick your games according to your own system - not according to the casino's planned influence.

But you must also be aware of the things you can do to increase your odds in a given game. We will discuss a couple of the most popular games.

Slot machines - Most slot machines have three reels. The number of combinations for lining them up depends on the number of symbols on each reel. Most machines have between 20 and 28 symbols per reel. To figure out how many combinations there are, you multiply the number of symbols on each reel times itself as many times as there are reels. For instance, the fewest combinations that there probably are on a three reel slot are: 20 symbols per reel with 3 reels - so we take 20 times 20 times 20 - or 8000 combinations. So theoretically a certain winning combination would, on the average, appear once in every 8000 spins of the reels.

Each machine can be set for a rate of payback. Let's say a quarter machine has a payback of 90 percent (the usual rate on quarter machines is 86 to 90 percent). That would mean that for every 100 quarters dropped into the machine it would pay back 90 quarters. The dollar machines often pay back between 97 and 99 percent.

The progressive slots are linked together so that a coin played in any of the link-up will increase the size of the jackpot. You don't have a chance at the jackpot unless you play the maximum number of coins. Since the large jackpot games must reduce the amount paid in smaller winnings, you would be better off playing other machines unless you are willing to put in the maximum and go for the jackpot.

The best odds are on the dollar slots. They usually have the greatest payback - as we said, payback is between 97 and 99 coins for each coin played.

Some slot methods to increase your odds of winning

Start out with only an amount of money you can afford to lose. Keep these coins separate from any other money, including your winnings. Play all your start-up coins. Now tally up your winnings. If you have less coins than you started with, go to a different machine, and using these coins start over. If you have more than you started with, put your start-up amount in your pocket. Then put an additional percentage in your pocket - 10 percent would be good, but whatever percentage you decide on, make the decision before you begin playing and stick with it. Now whatever you have left after pocketing those amounts you use for your start-up coins and begin again. Then in each additional round you will pocket half the winnings. As you can see, if you come out ahead in the first round and stick to the method, you will go home a winner. After the first round you will be playing strictly on winnings. If you don't come out a winner on the first round, you still have a chance to win and you will lose no more than the amount you originally decided you could afford to lose. But you need to be in control - this method will be of no help if you decide to change your rules in the middle of the game.

Another way to play the slots for better winning odds is to form a slot club with other players. Each person puts up a predetermined amount - make sure it is an amount each of you can afford to contribute regularly. The amounts put up should be the same for each player. Then you track the progressive games - you should track them for a while BEFORE you make attempts to win them. Keep records so you learn the characteristics of each progressive game. From these records, your team decides at what point each game is pregnant for a payoff. When the jackpot of a given progressive reaches that predetermined point, a team made up of some or all of the members takes the club bankroll and plays until they win or go broke. The key to winning here is to gauge the payoff point.

Slots are not easy to beat and the odds are NEVER in your favor but by putting yourself in control and using these techniques you will have a better chance of beating the odds than you had before.

Video poker

Video poker is a popular variation of the slot machine. But it is not a slot machine. The odds on a video poker game are greatly dependent on your skill as a player.

First, choose only those machines that pay full scale winnings. Each category of payoff is important, but a rule of thumb is 250 coins for a royal flush or 4000 coins for a royal flush under a 5 coin play. If the other payoffs are in line with the royal flush payoff, and you are a very skilled player, theoretically you could have odds VERY slightly in your favor. But you must know what you are doing.

For instance, when you are playing Video Jacks or Better - Keep any full house or better. Hold a flush or straight except when drawing to a four card royal flush. With a four card flush, three card royal flush, four card straight, three card straight flush, three of a kind, two pair, single pair empty your hand to these holds and draw to fill. Draw three to two high cards and draw four to one high card. Always play the maximum coins to take advantage of the bonus for a royal flush.

Black Jack

Black Jack is another very popular casino game in which it is possible to tip the odds VERY slightly in your favor, if you know what you are doing. It takes a serious and determined player to master the strategies to accomplish this, however. NEVER think that because you can tip the odds in your favor that you will win all of the time. EVERYONE loses some of the time so NEVER play with money you can't afford to lose.

Blackjack, as played in the world's casinos, has a number of variations - certain rules that apply in one casino may not apply in another. You will have to learn to adjust your game, if you travel from one casino to another. Some of the variations highly favor the casino, so to keep the odds favorable, you must avoid those variations and options that cut your odds.

OK. Most of the Black Jack games you will find are multiple-deck games. A single deck does give you slightly better odds. We will assume you are playing in a single deck game. With your new control, we will also assume you are playing with a bankroll that you have determined you can afford to lose. Now, you will need some real strategy to lower the odds against you.

First since the ace is countable as either one or 11, any hand you hold that contains an ace is a special hand - it can be counted low, with the ace as one, or it can be counted high, with the ace as 11. This two-way hand follows some special strategy rules.

First, start out counting it as a high hand. Then if the dealer's showing card is an eight, nine, ten, or ace, you should stand on a count of 19 or more and draw to a count of 18 or less. But if the dealer's showing card is a two, three, four, five, or six, stand on a count of 18 or more and draw to a count of 17 or less.

Using this strategy for a two-way hand, you will never stand until your count is 18 or more. When you draw to a two-way hand, if your high count goes over 21, you then begin a low count. At this point you will, in effect, no longer have an optional two-way hand so you will begin using the strategy for a regular hand.

The strategy for a regular hand is a bit more involved. Whether you stand or draw is always determined by the dealer's showing card.

If the dealer is showing a two, three, or four, you stand on 13 or more.
If the dealer is showing a five or six, you stand on 12 or more.
If the dealer is showing a seven, eight, or nine, you stand on 17 or more.
If the dealer is showing a ten or ace, you stand on 16 or more.

Notice that in using this strategy, you will always draw to a count of two to 11 and always stand on a count of 17 or more as long as you are not holding a two-way hand.

When you are offered the option of doubling down use it in this manner:

When you are holding nine, double down when the dealer is showing a two, three, four, five, or six. When you are holding ten, double down unless the dealer is showing a 10-count or an ace. When you are holding an eleven, always double down. When you are holding a two-way hand with a count of 12, 13, 14, 15,16, or 17, double down when the dealer is showing a six.

When you are offered the option of splitting pairs:

Split twos and threes when the dealer is showing an eight, nine, ten, or ace. Never split fours, fives, sixes, or tens. Split sevens when the dealer is showing two, three, four, five, six, seven, or eight. Split eights unless the dealer is showing a nine or ten. Split nines unless the dealer is showing a seven, ten, or ace. Never split tens. Always split aces when it is an option.

When you are offered the option of doubling down:

When you are holding a count of ten double down unless the dealer is showing a 10-count or an ace. When you are holding a count of eleven always double down. If you are holding a two-way hand with a count of 12, 13, 14, 15, 16, or 17, double down when the dealer is showing a six. Don't double down on other counts.

If you are offered the option of early surrender:

When the dealer is showing an ace, surrender 5, 7, 12, 13, 14, 15, 16, 17 unless you have a two-way hand. When the dealer is showing a 10-count, surrender 14, 15, 16 unless you have a two way hand. When the dealer is showing 9, surrender 6, 7, 9, 10.

If you are offered the option of insurance bets:

Don't use it unless you are a skilled card counter.

There have been some new options offered recently in some casinos. Be very wary of these, especially the ones with attractive pay-offs. Most of them have very poor odds for you.

It is a good idea to find a table where the casino is not doing too well. When you find a winning table, play it. There is, of course, no guarantee that the house loosing streak will continue.

You must exercise control. When you are having a day when the cards just aren't working, leave the table and go home. Under no circumstances increase your bets in hope of recovering losses. When you are having a good day and your cards are running strong, go ahead, increase your bets. When things begin to sour, leave the table and go home. Using this method, you will always cut your losses and always retain a portion of your winnings.

No strategy will work well if you don't know every rule. You must study and practice your strategy so that you can make the right decisions at the table. And remember, your bankroll should never exceed what you can afford to lose.

Travel

Every person at some time in his or her life will have a strong desire to travel. Whether it be a trip across state to visit Grandma or a fabulous trip to Italy, the need and desire is within just about all of us.

More people want to travel to adventurous and exotic places in far off lands. Sometimes movies and television are just not enough. We want to see some of the things we see on the screen for real!

Travel can be a great source of positive change in your life. Flying off to a strange new place can break you out of your rut. It can stimulate your mind in new ways and give you a new perspective on where you live once you return. Travel is a much needed respite from the same old daily cycle. Travel can be a break from raising children. A way to forget everyday worries. Travel can be a healing and strengthening process. Travel is an excellent way for us to find out what life had to offer us. it's a reminder about how fun and adventurous life can be. It can be a return to your youth.

The downside of travel is that it is expensive! The price of plane tickets alone keep most people on the ground. And once you get someplace, you still need to buy food, lodging, local transportation and lots of other stuff.

But there are many ways that you can travel for free. Thousands of people do it every day. In fact, there are many different methods and opportunities in the field of travel -- even ways to have people pay you while you go to the far off places you have always wanted to go. Let's talk about how you can do it.

Getting Paid to Travel

If you are a "die-hard" tourist, traveling can be a true blessing. Not everybody is cut out for a life on the road. Travel lacks the stability and security that can be found in a comfortable family home. It is probably not a good idea to start a family only to leave them behind while you ply the byways of the globe ... that is, unless you plan on taking them with you. But most often, a company will not want to pay for more than your ticket. If you have a family, they're usually out of luck when it comes to a free pass.

This is not to say that traveling has to be a lonely life. When you travel there are endless opportunities to meet people and make connections, and even find lifelong friendships.

The life of a paid traveler is filled with excitement and opportunity. You could meet someone who could help you advance your career like never before. Through traveling you meet a variety of people and you will undoubtedly run into many people who are "in synch" with you.

What are some of the jobs which will pay you to travel. Well, the obvious ones are pilots, bus drivers, stewardesses and people involved in traveling sales and marketing.

You can find many companies that are willing to pay your travel expenses in return for your professional skills. It's important to find a company that is interested in letting you travel on the job. If you are thinking about finding a job which involves travel, you can find out which firms participate frequently in this type of activity. Go to your public library and look up these books:

The Standard Industrial Classification. This is a manual published by the United States Government and it contains classification numbers for every kind of product, plus the name of companies you want to do further research on. Once you find the products and company which you will be interested in working with, find another publication called the Principle International Business Publication. Companies listed in the PIB have international trade interests with foreign companies and governments. Companies listed in the PIB contain products made with the SIC classification number, which you have already found. You have all the information you need to find a company which does business in the foreign locations you are interested in visiting. If some of these companies deal in products or services which match your skills, you may be ripe for a position that will afford you all the travel you have ever dreamed of.

Copy the addresses of the companies which spark your interest and write to them asking for their annual report. These reports should list all of the company's locations, foreign or domestic.

The next step is to give them a call. Chances are good you will reach a receptionist or secretary. Pick their brains! You will need to know everything you can about the company -- its products, the number of employees, their requirements and their overall goals and expectations. With some luck the secretary will give you loads of information. Armed with this kind of information, you can make a superb impression when you contact the company for a job interview. Keep in mind that employers are looking for enthusiastic, honest and friendly employees. Any additional skills you might have will be helpful, so be sure to mention them. If you are able to relate to people easily in a sincere manner, all the better. Make sure you give this impression during your interview. Overall, be sure to let your potential employer know that you are enthusiastic, flexible, serious about wanting to see new places and people -- and that you love to travel!

Jobs Which Offer Travel

There are worlds-filled with jobs that call for "paid travelers." Whatever your present line of work, there is likely some way you can parley your skills into a position that allows you to travel.
The Occupational Outlook Handbook published by the U.S. Department of Labor will be able to fill you in on a variety of marketing, sales and service jobs. This book will be available at your local library. If not, the library can locate it for you. The book contains information on more than 1,000 job classifications. Some of this information is about job qualifications, training, advancement in the workplace, competition, average earnings, related

occupations and each job's working conditions.

Some of the jobs that require travel are geologists, archeologists, antique and collectible buyers, travel agents, accountants, insurance claims adjuster and retail and wholesale buyers. These jobs are a small handful of employment that is available to you!

Getting and Airline Job

When you think of an airline job, pilots and stewardesses come to mind. The truth is, there are many more jobs available to you through the airline industry.

"Flying the Friendly Skies" is the quickest and one of the most luxurious ways to see the world. The benefits of working for an airline are the added bonus. Airlines allow free flights to their employees. Most of the time the immediate family is allowed to fly free as well, or at a greatly reduced price. When you are part of the flightcrew, you can visit various parts of the world and enjoy what it has to offer ... FREE!

Flight Attendants

Airlines look for certain qualities in flight attendants. More often than not, they are looking for someone who is friendly, responsible and enjoys his or her work. Most of all, you must love flying and meeting people.

A flight attendant must be at least 18 years of age, must be of "proportionate" weight, and must be between 5'2" and 6 feet tall. (You need to be tall enough to reach baggage compartments over the passengers to help them with their carry-on luggage.)

Decide which airline you would like to work for and call their personnel department to ask for an application. If the airline you reach says that they are not hiring at that time, ask if any similar airline is. They should be able to give you a lead on who is hiring.

Always be prepared to make copies of the application after you receive it. Practice with the first one while being careful to follow all instructions precisely. Keep one copy for your files.

Include a resume with your completed application. A resume will make you look more professional. Be sure to include all of your experiences and any special talents you might have. Any foreign language skills are extremely helpful. It is not necessary to be fluent, but you should be able to understand the basics of another language. Include any volunteer work you have done, as well as your experience in working with people. A good example of this might be a waitressing job or a retail position. If the airlines see that you have experience working with people, it will be a real plus for you! Use your resume to market yourself in a pleasant way. This may be the extra step you need to take in getting the interview you want.

What to Wear to an Airline Interview

Go to the interview looking as if you are already a flight attendant. You want the interviewer to see you just as you might look on the job. For men, a clean-cut appearance is the key. it is a good idea to be clean shaven. If you must wear a beard or mustache, keep them trimmed close. Wear a blazer, matching pants and nice shoes. You want to appear sharp and professional. Women should dress in a blazer with a matching skirt (knee-length) and low-heeled, closed-toe shoes.

Other Airline Positions

There are a variety of positions available with the airlines. Some of the jobs in customer service include reservation agents, ticketing agents, passenger service clerks, station agents and passenger service agents. Each of these positions requires that you deal with the public through ticket sales, assistance with the handicapped, answering flight questions and making sure they reach their destination with their luggage.

Positions in the flight crew include pilot, co-pilot and the flight engineer/second officer. All three of these positions require an FAA Commercial Pilot's License, FAA Flight Engineer's Certificate, FAA Airframe and Powerplant Mechanic's License, and or ATR. Instruments and/or multi-engine and instrument rating and an FCC Restricted Operator Permit.

There are also many positions available in flight operations, cargo/freight, clerical, data processing, finance, food services, maintenance, marketing and purchasing.

Go to the library to find the addresses of various schools for airline and travel careers, airline management, operations and personnel and travel agents.

Commuter Airlines, Regional Airlines and Domestic Carriers

If you are married and have children, commuter airlines are your ticket to a good family life. Commuter airlines allow you to have a schedule that would allow you to be at home each night. If you don't have a family, you will have lay-over opportunities to travel to some of the world's most exciting cities ... FREE!

Regional airlines span several states. This may give you an opportunity to visit your friends, relatives or just see different parts of the country. Domestic carriers are airlines that travel the entire United States. If you choose to be with a domestic carrier you won't be spending a lot of time at home. Most of these flights keep you away from home for several days at a time. Some of these airlines also fly to Canada and Mexico. If you want to spend time in certain parts of of the U.S., find an airline that serves that part of the country.

International Carriers

International carriers are those which fly regularly into foreign countries. With these airlines you will get credit for every hour that you are away from home. Credit hours accumulate whether you are flying, sleeping or eating as long as you are away from home. As a result, these credit hours tend to accumulate quickly. You are only allowed to be "in flight" for a certain amount of time each week. By the time your credit hours are at their maximum, you will be able to spend the rest of the month sightseeing or relaxing.

How To Become a Travel Consultant and Travel Free

Almost anybody can become a travel consultant. Housewives are able to work from their homes around their own time. It is a good source of "second income" and will aid in reducing the costs of family vacationing.

The job of travel consultant is ideal for retired people as well. This type of job can provide free vacations, extra income and a rejuvenation of youth and excitement. Senior citizens are a major group in the travel industry. People of the same age group with the same interests know how to help similar people, and what their fellow travelers are looking for.

The job of travel consultant is fun and easy. There are a few different ways to operate a travel consultant business. One way involves finding people who want to travel and bringing them into the agency. Whether you bring individuals or groups, you should be paid in the form of free travel or commissions. "Finders" are a good way to assist travel agencies by bringing in new business.

Another way to become a free travel agent is to organize a big group of people. Friends and relatives would probably like to take a trip with you. When you have a commitment from your group, visit the travel agency and ask to speak with the owner. Tell the owner that you are interested in booking a group which you have organized through the agency. In return, you mention that you would like to be the "tour guide" and have your expenses paid for. The travel agency has nothing to lose and everything to gain by getting the business of such a large group. This is an excellent way for you to take a trip ... FREE!

A final way to become a travel agent is to attend school for it. There are a variety of different schools which offer courses in travel agency related programs. Check your local library or high school counselor's office to find the addresses of these schools.

Cruise Ships

Cruise ships are often considered one of the most beautiful ways to travel. Unlike airplanes, you are able to experience a vacation by the scenic route. A cruise is a time to relax and enjoy your time. It is a vacation like no other.

Cruise ships offer a variety of ways for you to spend your time. They are almost like little cities on the sea. Most cruise ships offer swimming, sunbathing and shopping during the day and live entertainment during the evening. A cruise ship is an all-in-one vacation. You will be able to meet many new people while enjoying a beautiful view of the ocean with various islands.

Most cruise ships tend to travel in the southern part of the globe.

Cruise ship traffic is heavy in the Caribbean and Mediterranean areas. You will take an adventurous journey through various parts of the sea and then return to your point of departure.

Cruise ships offer a wide range of opportunities for employees. Each year their is a steady turnover of workers because once people see the world, they move on to other employment. Because the turnover rate is steady, chances for advancement are excellent if you choose to stay on.

The benefits offered by a cruise ship are spectacular!

Once you are hired, the employer pays for your flight to and from the ship's port. Most of the time cruise lines offer free medical and dental care. But best of all, you will be able to see the world and all of its excitement for FREE!

Employers in the cruise ship business will be looking for friendly, eager employees who will look forward to travel as well as meeting new people. You must be 18 years of age or older to even be considered for a job. If you think that you work well with and around people, this could be the job for you!

Some of the different positions offered by cruise ships include ... cruise director, assistant cruise director, host, hostess, social director, youths activities coordinator, sports director, tourist office assistant, shore excursion manager, disk jockey, musician and escort. The cruise ship staff is not the only one with available positions. The crew of this ship consists of waiters, cooks, maintenance workers and mechanics.

Advertisements for these kinds of jobs can be found in your college or city newspapers, on bulletin boards or heard on the radio. You may also be able to get information on these jobs from your local library, high school counselor's office or at a travel agency.

Railroads and The Bus System

Railroads are a scenic way to travel across the U.S. or Europe. Although our country does not rely heavily on trains for its transportation, it's still a viable and excellent way to travel.

AMTRAK has been looking for public support for trains, and is trying to sell more tickets to the public through travel agencies. Even if this isn't America's most popular form of transportation, it is still a beautiful way to tour the country. America's bus system doesn't seem to be a popular mode of transportation. Greyhound and Triangle lines are favorites among bus travelers. But bus traveling is inexpensive and scenic if you have all the time in the world.

More Ways to Cut Traveling Costs

There are ways to cut travel costs. Maybe you can afford a vacation trip!

Are you up to camping? If you camp along the way, you can get by pretty reasonably. You can save on hotel rooms and on meals. When you set up camp in the late afternoon, plan to eat at your campsite. It's fun, exciting, and inexpensive to eat outdoors. Since you will be carrying food with you for your evening meal, it will be easy to stop along the route during the day and make yourself a simple lunch, as well. You can also do breakfast in the mornings. Economical breakfasts are easy to find, however, so you may want to eat breakfast out.

If you do decide to camp as you travel, you will need to plan to stop early in the day. Campgrounds are often filled fairly early. It's a good idea to start looking for a campsite before 5 P.M. You will want time to set up camp and make your meal, anyway.

Where will you camp? There are nice campgrounds to be found in every state. Usually, you will find the most conveniences at commercial campgrounds, but you will pay more, too. State park campgrounds are very nice. Sometimes they don't have all of the conveniences that the commercial campgrounds have, but usually they are more reasonable. The most reasonable, and most beautiful in our opinion, are the state forest campgrounds. At these you will find very little in the way of conveniences. They usually offer what is called primitive camping - no showers. They do have a source of drinking water and restrooms with no water. Camping is probably the most economical way to travel, but it's not for everyone.

There are other ways to cut the expense of traveling, however.

If you plan to travel by air, go shopping! That's right. Did you think that there is a set rate for flying from one place to another. Not true. You will find that there can be a significant difference in the cost of airline tickets depending on the travel agent you are dealing with.

If you aren't too sure where you would like to go, ask what kind of bargain packages or discount deals they have going. You might find one that is perfect for you for a fraction of regular cost. Plan your trip well in advance. This way you can take advantage of any deals that may be in effect. Sometimes you can get discounts for buying your tickets in advance. Ask for discounted travel. Ask about flying standby. Standby is a little inconvenient but the price is less.

If the flight is overbooked, give up your seat. Usually you'll get a round trip ticket to anywhere in exchange.

Travel in the off season. You should be able to find discount trips during the off season. Ask at hotels for discounts - they often have discounts, but you will have to ask. If you are a senior citizen, be sure to ask for a discount for that, too. Just asking for an off season rate or asking for a senior discount will probably earn you a savings of 15 to 25 percent on your room!

Don't eat at hotels or obvious tourist establishments. You will find the least expensive meals at restaurants that depend on local trade.

Travel within your state. Free information on points of interest is available by writing to your State Department of Tourism. Plan ahead, though. It may take three to four weeks to get the information. You will probably be surprised at how many wonderful things there are to do within a hundred miles of where you live. Mini-trips can be a lot of fun and less draining on your budget.

If you are over 50-years old, the following books will help you plan your travel:

Unbelievably Good Deals & Great Adventures That You Absolutely Can't Get Unless You're Over 50 by Joan Heilman (Contemporary Books)

Get Up and Go: A Guide for the Mature Traveler
P.O. Box 50820, Department 6
Reno, NV 89513-9905

Financial Section
Need 20 Thousand Dollars Fast? You Can Get It!

So, you need a cool 20 grand real fast. You <u>must have</u> twenty thousand dollars today! But you also have a problem: your credit rating isn't all that great. If you walk into any bank, they might offer you two or three thousand, but without a cosigner or a major source of collateral, they aren't going to float you the 20 G's you need.

What to do?

Well, there's a way. There's always a way. Yes, you could have $20,000 in your pocket by the end of the day if you are willing to take a few risks and play your cards just right.

Listen to this true story:

Stan Renville was tired of his dead-end job as a laborer on a carpentry crew. He earned an okay wage, but what he really wanted was to be his own boss and to increase his income significantly.

Renville had his eyes set on a plywood and siding dealership which would allow him to buy low-cost materials at wholesale prices and resell them for high mark-ups. His work as a carpenter had taught him that demand was high for siding and remodeling materials. He knew the profit margin was excellent, and that if he could get his hands on $20,000 worth of inventory, he could quickly turn it around at almost three times the cost — $60,000 — a $40,000 profit for him!

His window of opportunity was small. He new a particular supplier that badly wanted to dump its siding and plywood inventory because it was expecting a major shipment of new materials any day.

Renville decided bold action was in order. He took out the yellow pages, looked up the addresses of 20 banks in his city and hit the streets. Starting early in the morning, he decided to get to as many banks as he could before the end of the day.

His goal was not to beg each bank for the full $20,000 but to seek a small, short-term loan of $2,000 or less from each one!

By midmorning, after visiting six banks, he had $10,000 in his checking account! After stopping for lunch, Renville continued through his tour of banks as he sought small, short-term loans. By two in the afternoon, he had all the money he needed — twenty thousand dollars.

Renville's quick work kept him ahead of the paperwork. It takes two or three days for loans to be processed, and each bank found no significant outstanding debt on his credit rating that day. Each bank gave him the small loan he sought without batting an eye.

But Renville knew he had to act fast — and with a bit of guts. He called up his wholesaler and placed an order for $20,000 in siding and plywood materials. Because he had lined up more than 10 individual construction contractors who wanted to buy materials beforehand, all he had to do now was call up each of them and secure a date for the material to be delivered.

With the individual sales secured, Renville drove down to the wholesaler, gave them his personal check for $20,000 and arranged for the items to be delivered to each respective construction sight. The next day, Renville got in his pick-up and paid a visit to each contractor and collected a check from each one. This time instead of asking for money, he was collecting it — at a 3 to 1 mark-up. By the end of Renville's second day, he had collected nearly $60,000 from resale of wholesale construction materials.

On day three, Renville paid a visit to his own bank, deposited the checks, paid off the dozen small loans he took two days earlier and spent the rest of the week enjoying the $40,000 in profits he had landed — all without a dime of upfront investment of his own money and with absolutely nothing for collateral.

It's a true story. With some guts, ingenuity and by bending the rules just a tad, Stan Renville made as much money in three days as most people earn in one or two years. He used his brains, took a risk — and did a lot of preplanning and homework. Renville made sure he had all the bases covered. He had the $20,000 in building materials pre-sold before he took the risk of taking out a dozen small loans for $2,000 or less.

Renville substituted brains, guts and old fashioned ingenuity for what he lacked in financial backing. He had a willingness to take a certain amount of risk — but he made sure he had a solid plan behind him to minimize the risk. He also wasn't afraid to bend the rules a bit, but did not step over into any illegalities.

Others have pulled off similar feats, using several sources of small loans to gather big money. One man, for example, pooled four credit cards, his own and the cards of a couple of willing friends, to put together $25,000 with which he bootstrapped his own recycling business.

You may be a lot closer to $20,000 or $30,000 right now than you think. Each of us has within us the ultimate wealth generator — the human brain. There's always an angle, there's always a way if you take a look at your assets, surroundings and life situation in new and creative ways.

Home Business

Are you tired of working that second job? Or are you in need of additional income, but you have ruled out a second job? Or are you just tired of working to make someone else rich and longing for an at-home income producing method?

Perhaps you've considered starting a business in your home but can't come up with an idea. "What can I do?" you have said, and you have not come with an answer.

Well, there have been thousands of people who have asked that same question of themselves - and found an answer. You can do it, too!

First, look to your skills, hobbies, and interests for some ideas - but you have to look at them from several angles. Yes, you say, but what if I don't have any that are marketable? Nonsense! You just aren't looking deep enough or from the right angle.

Most any interest can be turned into cash. For instance, a couple from Maine, who practiced thrift in their lives, turned that skill into a

$750,000 business within two years! How? By producing a newsletter for like-minded people. All it took to come up with the idea was looking at being a tightwad in a new and different way.

What are you interested in? Check out your hobbies and skills - usually they reflect your deepest interests. Crafts, woodworking, fishing - just about anything can be turned into a profitable business.

If your hobby involves making some unique item, you might consider marketing the product. Do a little research to find suitable outlets. Hobby and craft shops are not the only place you could market these items. Gift shops are often looking for unique items to sell. There are many other outlets depending on the item you make. Find a wholesaler willing to handle your product. If you like flea markets, you could market your products there. Or, like the "tightwads," you could start a newsletter for other people with the same hobby.

Or try the method a California couple use. Make how-to videos. Produce a video showing the methods you use to make your hobby items. Market them through the mail by advertising in hobby magazines. What could be better than receiving cash and checks in the mail every day?

You really like flea markets and garage sales? Set up your own garage sale or flea market business. People who don't like to hold garage sales but would like to recycle items need an outlet. Sell their items on consignment. Or advertise that you will buy their things so they don't have to hold a garage sale. Since you have an interest in these activities, you will know how much you can pay for the items and still sell them for a profit. Since they can sell all of their things in one lot and don't have to bother with having a garage sale, they should be willing to sell at a lower price.

Are you interested in cooking? You could start a catering business or home bake shop. A woman in Hawaii turned her interest in cooking and baking into a $500,000 catering business in less that thirteen years. Share your recipes and household hints through a newsletter.

You like to work in the yard, putter around with fix-it projects? Then you know about equipment for those activities. Start an equipment leasing service. How about a gardening newsletter?

Do you like to sew? A woman from California turned her interest in sewing into a stuffed-animal manufacturing and distributing business. If you come up with a unique idea, you could make a fortune - we all know about the cabbage patch doll phenomenon. Got a lot of sewing ideas? Do
a how-to video.

Are you into computers? Start a consultant business or a computerized imaging business. Do "how-to disks." You could start with "how-tos" about your interests or hobbies. Then you could talk to or interview other people and do "how-tos" about their hobbies.

As you can see, any hobby, skill, or interest can be turned into a money-making business with a bit of imagination. Nearly anything could be the basis for a newsletter, but don't let that be the stopping point when you are looking at your hobbies and interests with an eye for starting a business. It is very important to examine your ideas from new and different perspectives. It is the unique product or angle that is the easiest to succeed at. Uniqueness generates its own publicity - and publicity is a very good thing for a new business.

You really should try to stay with something you are interested in and know something about. Getting into a business that you know nothing about and trying to learn "on the job" is pretty risky. That's not to say you couldn't do it, but the deck is stacked against you. You will be surprised at how much you will have to learn even if you base your business on a hobby or other business that you think you know well.

It's important that you put a lot of thought, and perhaps some research, into your business before you begin. Know your product and know your market. Know who your prospective customers are. Remember, just because you have a deep and abiding interest in something doesn't necessarily mean that a lot of other people do. You must have a product or service that you can market to a lot of people if you are going to make money. And you have to have a pretty good idea how many people you can count on to buy your product or subscribe to your service if you are to set a price that you can make money on.

Look at the long-term prospects for your business. You will need to examine your idea in light of future trends.

For instance, the population of this country is aging. What does that mean in relation to your business plans? Well, products and services that cater to the elderly should stand a good chance of being successful. Health care will continue to be a big item. Home products and services should be a good business opportunity.

The environment will continue to be everyone's concern, and is likely to be a concern that will grow. A business in the field of environmental protection and/or energy conservation should be a good risk.

Computers are becoming a regular household item, and a very good learning tool for children. This is an expanding market.
Whatever your business, you need to know the trends and market your product accordingly. Try to appeal to existing trends. It's much easier than trying to create an interest in something people are not already anxious to accept. That's not to say it can't be done, but going with the trends will make success easier to achieve.

Have a plan! If you draw up a detailed business plan in advance, you will learn a lot about what will be involved in doing business. Planning how you will market your product and who you will market it to are just the beginning.

Ask yourself questions and write them down. Ask things like who will do the bookkeeping, when and where will it be done, how much space is this venture going to take, is there room in the garage or basement or can it be done from the kitchen table, how much start-up money do I need, can I depend on a steady income, do I have the funds to cover slow periods. And that's not all. You need to estimate what your income will be - do a five year plan. You need to estimate what your expenses will be - also do this for the five year period.

Are you asking, "How the heck do I know what the income and expenses will be for the next five years?" Call the Small Business Association (SBA) and the Service Corps of Retired Executives (SCORE). It doesn't cost you anything, and they will have loads of advice for you. Go for it! They can help you with your planning. How can you beat FREE professional advice?

While you are planning, work out the best way to get started with the smallest amount of money. You don't want to put any more money into it for start-up than you have to - you will need every extra dime you can scrape up for operating expenses and "emergency" funds. There will always be slow periods and unexpected expenses. If you can keep a little money "on the side," you will rest easier.

Wherever you can "cheap out," do it! Unless you are going into a business where public appearances are imperative, go the cheapest route. You probably don't need expensive, fancy office furniture or three-color letterhead. Look for used furniture or go to a discount house. Do you know someone who's in business or works in an office somewhere? Ask to see some of the catalogs they get in the mail. You can order printed stationery, envelopes, forms, and business cards for a pretty reasonable price - or check a local print shop.

Don't buy expensive equipment unless you are sure you will be needing it. For instance, you probably don't need a fax or copy machine right away. These services are available for a small fee without owning the equipment. Consider renting some of your equipment.

Do NOT begin any business without getting proper insurance coverage. Even if you think your business will not involve any risk, get liability coverage before you begin. One lawsuit could wipe you out - both your business and personally.

A good tax consultant is important. With a business, you will likely need help unraveling the tax laws. A good tax consultant can save you money. There are many tax laws that benefit the home business person. But those laws will do you no good unless you know how to use them.

No matter what your new business is going to be, you will likely have to "sell" it. Publicity is important. Do you know anything about selling and publicity? If not, BEFORE YOU PUT ANY MONEY INTO YOUR BUSINESS find out all you can about how to effectively promote your particular product or business. Publicity is a big expense as well as being vital to your survival. You might even consider hiring someone on a consultant basis to help you get the ball rolling. If you play your cards right, you may be able to get some free publicity - especially if you have a unique product or service to offer. Don't be shy! Unless you are extremely lucky the media won't come knocking on your door - they probably won't even be aware that you are there. You have got to let them know! Write up a little story or give them a call. Let them know where you are and what you are doing. If you aren't good at writing find a friend or someone who is. You don't need to write a book about it, just a couple of nicely written paragraphs will do.

OK. Ideas are important - but not everything. Once you have decided on the business you want to try, what else do you need?

Think positive. If you go into this business with an attitude of, "Well, I'll try it, but I probably won't make much money at it," well, then you probably won't. You must work on developing a positive attitude. Don't let that little voice inside your head defeat you.

Set goals - goals are very important to success. Why are goals important? When you know what you want, you'll know a good opportunity when you see it. With goals, you can more easily decide which opportunities you should follow up on. And you'll know where you are. You'll work harder to get back on track if you fall behind your established goals.

Do you have to work hard at your business? You must be willing to dedicate time to your business just as you dedicate time to your job and also be willing to go that extra mile. That "extra mile" may mean working at your regular job while you are getting going. In fact, we recommend that you do not quit your job until you get established and have a good steady income from your business. If you are planning to run this as a part-time business in addition to your regular job, you will have to decide how much time you are going to devote to this venture and then stick with it. If you are not self-disciplined enough to spend the time on it, your business will not prosper.

Are you going to have to put up with hardship when you start a business? Well, in addition to working a job and running a business, you may have to scrimp a little to get going, depending on the business you decide on. You will want to be very careful of the money you spend. Unexpected expenses have a way of popping up, and you should be prepared to meet them. But once you've got your business going with steady profits rolling in, won't the scrimping have been worth it?

OK. Hopefully we've got you thinking. Thinking is good. You will come up with a good idea. Or maybe you've already got a pretty good idea, but you're probably a little scared to try it. A little fear is fine - it'll help you think things through and plan carefully. And that's fine, too, as long as you remember that thinking will not overcome the fear - action will.

The nice thing about a hobby-based business is that it will be fun and interesting to you. And that very interest will be your ticket to success - it's much easier to stick with your time schedule and strive toward your goals if you have a real interest in what you are doing. People are always more successful at something they like and enjoy.

Investments
Financial planning

You have a savings account, a money market account, and some CDs. Isn't this all the investing you really need? No, not really. It's a good beginning - these things should certainly be a part of your financial planning. And they could be the sources of the money you could invest elsewhere - but you should always leave at least some funds in one or more of these safe and easily liquidated accounts - ready cash for emergencies. You pay for the safety and liquidity with lower earnings, though.

OK. The next step in your financial planning program should be to check out the retirement plans available to you. Retirement accounts generally offer safety but limited liquidity. Because of the limits on liquidity, your earnings will generally be better than the earnings on savings accounts and CDs. In addition, they offer legal "tax loopholes" that can save you money every year on your taxes.

The IRA (Individual Retirement Account) is available to every employed American. You establish an IRA by depositing money with an institution that has been approved by the government for handling these accounts. It is rather like your savings account but with stricter regulations. You will be well advised to keep records and pay attention to dates.

You are eligible to invest in an IRA if you or your spouse has earned income or receives alimony payments. Earned income is wages or salary from an employers. It can also be earnings from self-employment - the self-employed also have other plans available to them.

You have a limit on the amount you can contribute to your IRA each year. You cannot contribute more than your earned income for the year. You may not contribute more than $3000 per year. If you and your spouse both work you may each open an account and each contribute $3000. You may have an IRA even if you have a pension plan at work, a Keogh or a 401(k).

Whatever type of IRA you have, it is tax deferred - you don't have to pay taxes on the interest it earns until you withdraw the money. This means your earnings will grow faster than they would in a regular savings account at the same rate of interest. And then you can add to this the savings you will realize from being in a lower tax bracket when you start withdrawing. As you can see any IRA gives you the advantage of a "double tax loophole."

The deductible Individual Retirement Account is one of the most advantageous retirement plans available. If you are eligible to open a deductible IRA, you have a triple advantage. With a deductible IRA, you may deduct the amount that you have contributed to your account from your gross income when you do your income taxes. You do not pay taxes on the amount that you have put in your IRA, you do not pay taxes on the interest earned, and you will save by being in a lower tax bracket when you do withdraw the money. A triple tax loophole!

Do you qualify for a deductible IRA? You need to look at two things - your income level and your other pension plans. If you are eligible to open one, you should - it's one of the best retirement investments you can make.

However, if you have a 401 (either k or b) available to you at work and your employer matches or partially matches your contribution to it, you'll probably do better with it than with the IRA. In addition to the company's matching funds, your 401 is guaranteed to be deductible whatever your income level. A 401 is convenient and easy. The amount you designate is deducted from your paycheck and invested for you. You don't pay taxes on the deducted portion of your wages, the interest earnings are tax-deferred, and some employers contribute matching funds or a percentage of your contribution. You have the advantages of the same triple tax loophole as the IRA offers PLUS your employer may also contribute funds for you.

Keoghs are retirement plans for the self-employed or part-time self-employed who are also employed. Earnings on Keogh plans are deferred like earnings on IRAs. Keoghs are deductible for everyone - no matter what your income or what other pension plans you have. And you can contribute much more - up to $30,000 per year as long as it doesn't exceed 25 percent of the income you get from self-employment. Keogh plans are complicated, requiring a great deal of monitoring so you don't run into trouble with the IRS. If you have employees, the rules are even more complicated.

As an alternative to deductible IRAs, you might consider annuities sold by insurance companies. Annuities also accumulate deferrable earnings. You can invest as much as you like in annuities - the IRA limits don't apply. You do, however, have to pay a penalty for early withdrawal, as you would with IRAs. Annuities may not be as attractive as IRAs because the sales charges will cut into your returns.

Another alternative is tax-exempt bonds. The advantage with these is you never have to pay taxes on the earnings. The bonds, however, have little growth.

If you have kids you want to send to college, consider the old-fashioned Series EE U. S. Savings Bonds. The returns aren't so great, but the earnings are tax-deferred and they are state tax exempt. Don't carry them in your child's name, because if they are in your name and you redeem them to cover college tuition and fees, the interest is tax free (if you meet the income guidelines). This makes the Series EE an excellent and safe place to invest money that is ear-marked for college.

Tax exempt investments are a smart investment - when you don't have to pay federal income tax on the interest, your realized earnings mount up. For instance, if you're in the 31 percent federal tax bracket, a 7 percent tax exempt rate is about equal to or better than 10 percent taxable rate. Municipal bonds and municipal bond funds can provide both federal and state tax exemptions.

OK. We'll assume you have adequate life insurance to protect your family in case of your death. We'll also assume that you have a sufficient amount invested in retirement funds. Now, if you have enough money in safe accounts to allow you to withdraw investment funds and still have a ready-cash reserve, this may be the time for you to check out investments. But be sure you are not investing cash you need to cover your commitments. Investments involve a degree of risk - you should not count on your investments to cover basic needs.

For newcomers, investing in the stock market can be a bewildering (and sometimes costly) experience. It's important to prepare yourself before you make the plunge. Read and study market information - have a basic idea of what the market is all about. This is important. After all, you are putting your money into it. If you have a basic understanding, it won't be so scary to get your feet wet. How to Buy Stocks by Louis Engel and Brendan is almost required reading - we highly recommend it. Or go to your library and look over some of the other very good books on the subject. While you're there, look over some of the magazines featuring stock market information and advice. You may find some that you would like subscriptions to. You don't have to become an expert before giving the market a try, but as we said, you should have a basic understanding of market workings. And once you're actually investing it is important to keep well informed.

When you feel you are ready to get your feet wet in the stock market- go in on the buddy system. Find a full-service broker. Being inexperienced, it's important for you to get yourself a full-service broker. Unlike the discount brokers, the full-service variety will advise and assist you. You will pay more for full-service brokerage than you would for discount brokerage, but for newcomers the service is worth it. Ask friends or acquaintances for recommendations and talk with the brokers before you decide on one. You will want to find one you are comfortable with and one whose market approach you agree with.

Always keep in mind that the broker is working on commission - their advice may not always be as good for you as it is for them.

The more business they have moved through your account, the more fees they can charge you. Remember, YOU are always the ultimate decision maker.

When you have decided on a broker, they will advise you on the steps to take to open an account - an easy procedure - and on how to get started. Then you will make a stock purchase. Purchasing stock can usually be done by phone. Your full-service broker will be able to advise you on the type of order to place but be ready to make decisions. Ultimately, he will follow your instructions.

Consider joining an investment club. This is a great way to learn about the market. You will be researching and investing as a group - which can be comforting. Investment clubs can be a very successful and pleasant way to enter into market investing.

Does your place of employment offers a stock purchase plan to employees? It could be a good place to begin your investing. It's convenient, easy, and often employees are offered a discount on the stock they purchase. Two things to consider: Do you think your company is headed for success? Are you limiting your investment? You want to be relatively confident that your company will be successful, and you don't want more than 20 percent of your investment capital tied up in a single company.

Consider mutual funds. Mutual funds are easy. Just call the mutual fund company and ask for an application. Some discount brokerages offer a mutual fund buying service. Mutual funds involve minimum risk, offer diversification, don't require a large investment, and are easy for you if you know little about stocks and have little time to spend in keeping informed on the market. Your profit potential is limited, however. If you do decide to go with mutual funds, choose carefully. Not all are equally successful. Look for one with a good track record. When you find a good one, keep in mind that there are no guarantees. A good past record doesn't preclude mistakes in the future.

A discount brokerage is a good choice if you know what you are doing and can make most of your own investment decisions. You can save a lot on commissions, but we recommend a full service brokerage for newcomers.

OK. So, how do you decide what to buy and when to sell? Well, it depends on your style. Even the pros don't all use the same methods. You will develop a style over time. Some of the methods used are:

Diversification - buy a range of stock and other investments rather than put all your money in one. This is for your protection. If you hold a range of stock and one fails, you will have the others to protect you from total loss. If you hold a variety of investment types, you will again be protected from a poor showing in one area.

Interval investments - put a certain amount of money into a stock at regular intervals. You don't "time" the market, but buy at given times whether the stock is up or down. With this method, you don't always get in on the lowest price, but you don't invest all your money when the stock is at it's highest either. It helps you to avoid buying on impulse.

Set a sell price - determine in advance at what price you will sell a stock. Decide how much gain you want to achieve or how much loss you are willing to sustain and set those as a sell price. You will be relieved of making these decisions during future fluctuations of your stock. This will help you to avoid over-reacting to the shifting conditions of the market. Even the pros sometimes over-react.

Sell to reinvest - when a better investment comes along, sell to take advantage of the new investment. If a stock you are holding isn't going anywhere and you have determined another is a better opportunity, you may want to sell the dud and pick up the better one. Don't do this on impulse, but after checking it out. Don't change your investments too often - the commissions will eat up your profits.

Set long-term investment goals. Be patient. Don't bounce around from investment to investment looking for the instant "pot-o-gold". Chasing that pot-o-gold, you may be taking a lot more risk. Remember if the yield is high, the risk is high. Establish a long term plan that can ride out insignificant declines in the market.

Invest in various types of securities - as we mentioned earlier, keep some funds in savings accounts and CDs. You may also want to check out municipal bonds, Treasury bonds, and corporate bonds. Be careful, but don't be too conservative. A percentage of your funds should be in the safe lower return categories, but a generous portion should be invested in less safe capital-appreciation securities.

Stay involved - know what is going on with your investments. Keep up with market conditions. Understand your investments - understand the companies you are dealing with and what conditions will affect your investments. Don't get too caught up in it. You should be in control of your investments - your investments should not be in control of you. You should be very wary of investments you do not understand. As a newcomer you are at risk of being taken advantage of - talked into risks you are not aware of.

Be aware of the tax implications - know what taxes will do to your earnings. But look at more than just the amount of taxation. Figure in the tax to arrive at an adjusted yield. Then consider your other options. Your adjusted yield may be higher than yields from tax-free investments, so don't limit yourself to the tax-free options just to avoid paying taxes.

Common stocks are probably the best easily available investment over the long haul. They have proven to perform better, over all. Of course, this is not to say that you are guaranteed to make money in stocks. The proven performance is a performance average. Individual stocks can and do perform very poorly. If you happen to be holding one of those, the average performance of stocks will be of no help to you.

But you cannot lose more than your total investment in common stock. And you have a good chance of getting a good return on your money. Your profits can be in dividends or a change in the price of the shares you hold. Dividends can be paid regularly, irregularly, or not at all. The change in the price of the shares is also a profit (or loss). But one that you realize only when you sell them.

If the market price of the stock you hold drops, you don't actually lose money unless you sell. If you hold out and the stock price rises and surpasses your purchase price and you sell, you have made money. It sounds very simple. You merely hold until it rises again. But what if it doesn't come back up? The trick is to be able to gauge whether it will rise again, and if not, get out with the least loss possible. Not easy.

One method of playing the high-risk stocks is to invest in a start-up company with good potential for growth - a small or new company with a big idea, an experienced management team, and a reasonable financial footing. Buy no more than what you can reasonably afford to lose and set a sell limit to cut your losses if the stock should drop. Or choose a company that is planning to market a new product that you feel will be a winner and go with it.

Another method is to choose a company that has dropped but now has new management or has renewed potential for some other reason. Perhaps you see potential in telecommunications, health-care paper-pushers, computer networking, or the international trends. If you are very astute and informed as to future trends, you could get lucky and ride a stock to riches. Microsoft, for instance. A mere $32,000 investment in Microsoft in 1986 was worth $1 million in 1992!

These are very high risk methods of investing which is why the potential rewards are better. Risky, but it has been done. Be aware, though, that the Microsoft's of stock investments are rare. If you can't afford the loss, stay with the more secure, lower return investments. It is important to try to invest so that your money will grow faster than inflation.

Always Look for Highest Return

When you invest money in anything, even a savings account or annuity, look for the highest return possible.

An annuity -- purchased through your insurance agent -- will probably give you a higher yield than a savings account and with about the same safety factor. If you can get a one percent or even half percent higher rate, go for it. If you are scoffing at this and saying, "One percent is hardly worth shopping around for," let;s see how much difference that small percentage can make.

Let's say you want to invest $1,000 for your new baby to begin a retirement fund for him. Let's look at the difference a half percent or one percent can make:

| 5% | 5.5% | 6% |

---

50 years	$12,362	$15,513
$19,935		
60 years	$20,443	$26,844
$36,271		
65 years	$26,288	$35,312
$48,924		

INSURANCE

Do you think insurance is too costly? Have you dropped your insurance coverage to save the money?   Are you deliberately under-insured to reduce your premiums?   Have you thoroughly checked over your policies to make sure you are thoroughly and adequately insured?

If you answered "yes" to any of the first three questions or "no" to the last one, the following information could save you thousands of dollars. Actually, no matter how you answered the questions, you will probably be surprised at the information.

First of all, if you have children, if you own anything, if you do anything, you NEED insurance. Why? To protect your children, to protect what you own, and to protect what you earn now and will earn in the future.

If you have children, you should carry life insurance on yourself to protect them. It will be difficult and expensive for your family if you die.   You should make sure that they have adequate funds to survive while they make the adjustment to the change. How much? Probably about five to seven times what you earn annually. If you are a housewife or househusband, you still need coverage. How much would depend upon what it would cost to hire someone to take care of the house and children for the next five to seven years.

Shop around. Rates vary from company to company, and there are several different types of life insurance. Ask the insurance people you visit with to fully explain the policies they sell. When you do buy, make sure you know and understand your policy, Check to see if you can get a better deal if you purchase a policy that insures both you and your spouse.

If you own anything, you should carry replacement insurance for it.

This should include coverage in case of fire, theft, loss, or weather damage. Even if you rent an apartment, you need insurance on your personal property and furnishings. Don't depend on the apartment owner's insurance. He may have little or no insurance that will benefit you. If you own your home, your policy should cover your house and other buildings, as well. Understand your policy. Make sure it covers what you think it does. Be sure the weather damage includes wind, hail, flooding. If you are in a quake area, check to see if you have coverage for quake damage. And, just being insured for these things is not the whole answer. Make sure you are adequately covered.

For instance, if you have a mortgage on you home, your lending institution probably requires a minimum amount of insurance coverage. That should be enough, right? Wrong! They are only concerned about covering the loan - protecting themselves. You need enough coverage to protect yourself, too. In case of extensive damage or complete destruction, you will want to restore or replace your home as well as pay the lender.

Your personal property and furnishings policy should provide for replacement of your items, not the current market value. Current market value does not even pay you what you paid for the items. It is figured on the purchase price and then depreciated for each year since you bought the item. In effect, for many items you will be paid next to nothing. You need to get enough to replace the items. This is called replacement insurance. Replacement insurance costs a little more, but after all, the cost of replacing your property in case of a disaster or theft is the reason you carry the insurance.

Find out what kind of risks your personal property is insured against and make sure all of your things are insured. Sometimes particular types of things - like jewels, art, furs, watercraft, snowmobiles, computers, home-office equipment - have limited or no coverage on a regular policy. You can purchase policy endorsements to extend or increase coverage.

Go through your house or apartment room by room and make a list of everything. Take this list, complete with photographs and estimated cost of replacement to your insurance salesman. Discuss it with him. Make sure you have adequate coverage. Then keep this list in a safe place - not in your home where it might be lost or destroyed if your property is stolen or damaged. The list will help you deal with adjusters, if you need to make a claim. Whenever you buy a new insurable item be sure to talk to your insurance person about it AND ADD IT TO YOUR LIST.

OK. So you have insurance on yourself, your home, your personal property; that should be about it, right? No, sorry, that's definitely not enough.

Have you noticed how "sue-happy" people seem to be? And, worse, the outrageous settlements that are being awarded? Think you don't have to worry about it? Well, you do. You are at risk. We all are at risk - any one of us could be sued for thousands of dollars over some minor accident or injury that we may not even really be responsible for - and you could lose your home, your car, and any other assets that you have.

If you own a car that is involved in an accident, you can be sued - even if you aren't the driver. If you own a house or other property, you can be sued if someone gets injured while on your property - even if that person was there without your express permission or invitation.

You need insurance coverage to protect what you own. Even if you don't own much, you need to protect what you are earning now and what you will earn in the future. You need liability insurance. The good news is that liability insurance is cheap.

If you have automobile insurance, you probably have liability insurance included in your policy. That's a good start but only a start. First, check the extent of your coverage. It probably looks like a lot, but just as probably, it isn't enough. The required minimums in most states are inadequate. Consider the outrageously large settlements awarded to people. Then, consider the damages that are possible if your car goes out of control. Remember that when settlements are awarded, you are responsible for the amount that your insurance doesn't cover. Don't be misled by the common belief that people can't sue you for more than your insurance would cover. That just isn't true. People have lost their homes and all their assets and even a portion of their future earnings in lawsuits, because they didn't have enough insurance coverage to pay the damages. Still think your coverage is adequate?

Increasing your liability coverage isn't awfully expensive. The more you buy, the cheaper per thousand it is - so if you double what you already carry, the price won't double.

Also make sure that your insurance will cover no matter who is driving your car. You never know when someone may borrow your car. You know how things seem to happen. If someone who isn't insured just takes the car around the block, there's sure to be an accident. Make sure, too, that you have coverage for you and your passengers if you are involved in an accident with an uninsured motorist.

Auto liability is an absolute must, but you'll need liability on your property, too. You need coverage to protect yourself from being sued by anyone who is injured on your property. The injury does not necessarily have to be your fault. It can just be the result of an accident. But if it happens on your property, you are at risk. Again, check to see that you have an adequate amount of coverage.

You also need to know if your liability policy covers special situations in your life-style. For instance, if you conduct a business in your home, you may need a different policy or an endorsement on your present policy. You may not think you conduct a business in your home, but if you have a home-office or do some babysitting in your home, it may be viewed as a business.

Having employees may require a change in your policy, too. Think you don't have any employees? Think again! A youngster who cuts your grass or a person coming in to clean one morning a week or someone coming in to sit with your children may be considered employees. Check to see if you need a policy endorsement.

If you have contractors working on your place - remodeling, repairing, landscaping, or whatever - make sure they have liability insurance AND worker's compensation insurance. If they don't carry insurance on themselves, you could be sued in the event of an injury! Make sure they are covered before you let them begin working.

By now you are probably thinking, "Wow! All this coverage will cost a fortune!" Well, liability insurance is not really very costly and it protects you from the loss your car, home, assets, and even future earnings. Extended, extra, and umbrella liability is a bargain. You'll probably find that automobile insurance is rather costly, but homeowners insurance, and personal property coverage isn't too bad.

You can save on your insurance costs if you:

(1) Ask your state insurance department for a list of insurance companies and their prices.

(2) Shop around and talk to several insurers before you buy.

(3) Check into buying all you policies from one company.

(4) Ask about an "extra liability umbrella."

(5) Ask about special discounts.

One disaster or being sued one time could mean losing everything you own. Make sure you are protected.

OK. Perhaps the most important insurance is health insurance. Yes, we know, health coverage can be expensive. But medical cost are REALLY expensive - they can wipe you out with one major hospitalization. In addition, if you have health insurance you are assured of the best care a hospital has to offer. Without insurance, you could even be turned away at some hospitals.

So, what do you do? Well, you shop around. And you learn about health insurance so you know what it is you are buying. Even if your employer offers a health plan, you would be wise to check it out and see what kind of coverage you have. It is getting more and more difficult for employers to keep up with the rising costs, so they may be cutting back on your coverage. Be sure you are well covered.

If your employer does offer a health plan, it's probably the best deal for the bucks you will find. But know what the coverage is. If it isn't sufficient, you might want to look for supplemental insurance.

Also, if you are worried about a possible layoff, you are probably worried about your coverage. Check with your employer to see if you are covered by the Consolidated Omnibus Budget Reconciliation Act. If you have health coverage and your company employs more than nineteen, you should be covered. This act guarantees you an option of continuing group health coverage for eighteen months after termination.

If you have no group coverage available to you, you will have to go looking for a policy on your own. Lucky you! It's going to cost you - but as we said, no one should be without health insurance. If you and your family have no pre-existing conditions and can fly through physical examinations with no problem, you may be able to find good insurance that is less expensive - not inexpensive, just less expensive.

If you do have pre-existing conditions, you may have to settle for a policy with a rider that excludes that condition for a time. It's not a good idea to settle for one that excludes it for your lifetime, however.

Most policies will offer you some option on what they call deductible. A deductible is an amount that you must pay to the hospital before your insurance will kick in. Naturally, the higher the deductible, the lower the premium. Think carefully before you agree to a large deductible to get a lower premium. Also, be sure to check on how the deductible works. For instance, if your policy is $1000 deductible - is that $1000 per individual or per family? Usually there is a family limit so that if you have nine family members, you wouldn't have a $9000 deductible in family bills. Know what you are getting.

No matter what kind of insurance you have - even if its through your employer - you need to know what the maximum coverage is. Even if the maximum looks quite large, remember that hospital bills can build up to as much as $200,000 or more in short order. If your insurance maximum isn't AT LEAST that much, check out supplemental major medical insurance. The cost shouldn't be excessive.

Don't consider any other supplemental insurance. Dread disease insurance is so limited and usually specifies such conditional rules that you will seldom, if ever, benefit from it. Good health insurance is costly enough, don't spend your money on insurance that will be of little or no benefit.

If you have a serious or chronic existing condition, you will be hard-pressed to find a good health insurance policy at a price you can afford. It's going to be difficult. Check with your state insurance department. They may be able to give you some help. Some states have special insurance programs for the hard to insure. You may have to show proof of rejection - applications to mainstream companies that have turned you down.

Health insurance is a bummer, but you should have it. In fact, you should have a regular coverage and major medical coverage. It will take a bite out of your earnings, but if you become ill and are taken to a hospital, you can say, "Yes, I have insurance, and yes, I have major medical coverage." You'll be able to afford the best care they can give you.

Being underinsured or not insured at all is not worth the risk even if it does save you some money on premiums. In the long run, it may cost you thousands of dollars.

Save Money When You Buy That New Car

Planning to buy a new car? With a little knowledge of the car business, you can save a bundle.

First, shop around. Don't buy at the first dealership you visit, at least not on your first visit. Salesmen want to sell you a car, and they know their chances of selling you a car diminish greatly if you don't buy on your first visit. So don't be anxious - let them be anxious.

Your first visit to each dealership should include enough time to look over the cars, talk with the salesmen, and even talk about price.

Even if you fall in love with a car, don't fall for the salesman's line. He can give you a better price than he will offer you on your first visit. Let him know you are serious about buying a car, though it may not be this particular car - unless the price is right. Just politely tell him you need to think about it or make some other polite excuse and leave.

Be courteous. If this is the car you want, you'll be seeing him again. Return in a few days. You'll have more negotiating power then, and you'll find they are more willing to agree to your terms.

And what should those terms be? Well, let's back up a little. First of all, to car salesmen pricing is a game. Rarely do any two people pay the same for a particular model. The sticker price on a new car is not the price that the salesman or the dealer expects to get. Of course, if you are willing to pay it, they will take it and chuckle all the way to the bank. But they expect you to play their game. If you play well, you can save a lot of money.

OK. So what should you pay? It depends upon what kind and model of car you are buying. It also depends upon whether you are looking at a Plain Jane (a car with no optional accessories) or one fully decked out with accessories. You can figure that what the dealer charges for accessories is probably around three times what he paid for them - sometimes more. The dealer add-ons are even more outrageously priced - up to a beyond a hundred times the cost. For instance, a pin stripe that costs the dealer about $10 will probably be priced at over $100.

So, you can easily talk him out of the add-ons - they should very willingly throw them in free because their actual cost is less than one-tenth of the price they've put on them.

If the add-ons are thrown in free, you're back to the basic sticker price. Do you pay this? Absolutely not! Now is when you begin to really negotiate. Subtract the dealer's prep charge from the sticker list price and then subtract $3 to $5 thousand from that. That's your beginning offer. Don't be afraid of dipping too low - you can always come up later. The salesman will probably dazzle you with figures jotted on paper or popped out of a calculator and he'll probably call the manager in. Just stick to your price. They may even haul out an invoice to show you what they paid for this car. Don't believe it! The invoice won't reflect special rebates and discount that the dealer gets.

If they don't agree to your price, now is the time to make your polite excuses and leave. When you return in a few days, they will be more willing to negotiate. If their price doesn't come even close to yours, come up a little - maybe $500. Don't be too eager. You can always make another polite get-away and come back again in a few days.

Once you decide to buy the car, or maybe even during the dealing, you will be offered an extended warranty. The prices on warranties are also inflated (about three times the dealer cost). During your negotiations you might have them throw in that warranty at no extra cost, if you are interested in purchasing it. After all, it only costs them about one-third of what it'll cost you.

Your actual total cost will depend on your negotiating skills, the salesman and dealership you purchase from, and the type and model of car you buy.

If you are following up on advertised new car prices, be forewarned. Those prices do not necessarily reflect the price range of the car you want. Often the really low advertised price is for a Plain Jane (the one without accessories). This is not a car they really want to sell you, either. That price is advertised to get you in the door. The car they really want to show you and sell to you is the one with all the accessories. It's not hard to figure out why when you know the percentage of profit they realize on accessories.

What about your trade-in? The reason we haven't mentioned it until now is that you shouldn't trade in a car if you want to get your best deal. Most of what you would get for your trade-in you'll get anyway as a cash discount or just allowed in negotiating. So, don't trade in. Take the time and effort to sell it yourself and come out a few more bucks ahead.

To get the most money for your used car, you need to invest a little time - and maybe a minimum amount of money to get it looking classy. Your first step is to wash and polish it. We don't mean just running it through the car wash. Take a cotton swab to all the tight little corners, polish the windows and the tires, polish the chrome, shampoo the carpeting and upholstery. Most people looking at cars believe that a car that looks good is good. It looks well cared for. Besides even those people who buy a used car like to get something nice that they can be proud of.

Just a bang-up cleaning job will help you get a better price, but don't ignore an oil change, grease job, and general maintenance items. These things, too, show that your car has been well cared for and will help you fetch a better price for it. Really major repairs, though, don't pay. You will probably spend more to do them than you could expect to get back in increased value of the vehicle.

To determine the value of your car, check the book value at your bank or at the library. If you have a lot of extras on your car or if it is truly in top condition - both in appearance and mechanically- you might want to price it higher than average. Ask a couple of new-car dealers what they would pay you if you sold it out-right to them. But remember, this is the price they would give you - not the price they would sell it to their customer for. After a few inquiries, you will have a good idea what the value of your car is. It's a good idea to add a little to that to leave you room for bargaining - many prospective buyers will pass up even a good deal on a car if they can't "talk your price down a bit." It's a matter of pride in their technique, maybe.

When a prospective buyer calls you about the car, be honest. It is a waste of his time and yours if you promise something that is obviously not there. When the customer has looked it over, he may want a test drive. You and your insurance company are liable for any accidents so be careful. Ask to see the buyer's driver's license. You might want to ride with him. Or you might want to hold the keys to the buyer's car. Once you and the buyer have reached an agreement, make two copies of a bill of sale including the words "as is, with no implied warranties". Have the buyer sign one for you to keep for your files. Ask for cash, money order, or certified check. You don't want to get stuck with a bad personal check. You may want to accompany the buyer to the Department of Motor Vehicles Office to make sure title is transferred promptly - you don't want any nasty liability surprises a couple of months later.

Assuming that your have nailed down a satisfactory deal on a new car, don't sit back and relax just yet! You can also save money on the financing of it. Don't automatically finance at the dealership. Shop for a loan at a bank or credit union. Pick the best interest rate offered.

Or look to your home equity. The interest on these loans is just above the prime rate and since you get tax breaks on home loan interest, the actual cost of the loan is lowered. It can be the cheapest source of money you will find.

Or you may be able to borrow from your 401 (k) or other retirement plan or even your profit sharing plan where you work or your life insurance plan. Borrowing in this manner is actually borrowing against your own resources. The loan is quick and easy. There's no credit check and often the loan can be accomplished with a phone call. Since there's no real risk to the lender, the interest rate is very low.

Borrow against your savings. Sometimes it is wiser to borrow against your savings than it is to simply withdraw the money to pay for a purchase. But if you will be assessed an early-withdrawal penalty, it could cost you more than a loan will cost. When deciding on this procedure, you will have to take into account the rate of interest your savings will continue to earn and the rate of interest you'll have to pay on your loan in addition to early-withdrawal penalties.

Or take out a margin loan. You can use your securities as collateral for a car loan. If you do this rather than sell your securities , you can avoid the tax liability for selling.

When setting up the loan, ask for bi-monthly payments. You could save a bundle! Bi-monthly simply means that you make a payment twice a month. No, we're not suggesting that you pay more per month. For example, if your loan payments would be $600 per month, ask for a schedule at $300 twice per month. This kind of payment schedule might even be easier for you to meet. Make sure that the lender will deduct the payment in such a fashion that the principal will be reduced on the payment date. In that way you will be saving two weeks of interest every month. That adds up. If you have also secured a low interest rate, perhaps by borrowing against your 401(k), you have an ideal car loan set-up.

NEW HOME

Thinking about buying a home?

Most of us still have that same urge to "own a little piece of land" that our forefathers had. Owning a place of our own somehow gives you a sense of security. Pride of ownership can't be overlooked either. Some of us yearn for a place to raise kids or a place to raise a garden or just a place to do a little tinkering and fixing. If you have a place of your own, you can remodel and paint and fix at will - you can stamp it with your own personality. Once you have made it your own by changing its appearance to suit you,

you feel more comfortable and secure in it. You feel you belong. These are all good and valid reasons for buying a home.

You may also feel that a home is a good investment because you will be getting something tangible for the money you are "just throwing away on rent" now. You may feel the property will be sure to appreciate in value, and when you are ready to sell, you will realize huge profits. These reasons for purchasing a home may be a little more shaky than the first reasons are. The reasons could very well be valid, but certainly your assumptions are not guaranteed to work out the way you expect them to.

First, it is true that you will be getting something tangible for the money you are now spending on rent. However, your monthly output for housing could end up being a lot more than you are now spending. It all depends on your situation.

Even though your anticipated house payment may be about the same or even less than the rent you are paying, you could still end up paying more per month. How? Well, your utility bill may be larger. Do you pay all of your utility bills separately from your rent or are some included in the rent payment? In a house of your own, none of the utilities are included in the payment. In addition, your utility bills may run higher, especially if you are moving from an apartment or a small rental house. Also, all of the maintenance - yard and house - will have to come out of your pocket. Yard maintenance may seem like a small matter, but it is not. You will have to purchase equipment to care for the yard and that requires maintenance, too. On the other hand, mortgage interest is tax deductible so you will save some on your taxes. Be sure to figure the tax savings into your calculations when you compare your rent expense against the cost of owning a home.

As far as the property increasing in value to give you huge profits when you are ready to sell, there are no guarantees. What property values do today (whether they are increasing, maintaining, or decreasing in value), may not be the same as what they will do next year or the year after. It all depends on supply and demand, and that balance can change rapidly in any community.

However, we are not trying to discourage you from buying a home. As we said, there are many valid reasons for wanting a home of your own. We just want you to know that some of your expectations could be footed in shaky ground.

When you decide to buy, go into it carefully. Don't overstrain your budget. It can be a real temptation to buy the very best home possible and use the maximum loan power your lending institution will grant you. It is easy to think that you will surely get raises and promotions in the years to come. When you are in the "home buying fever," it is also easy to think that this is the most important purchase you will ever make so you want to get the very best you can.

But be sure to include the other side of the coin. Are you depending on two incomes? What if one of you looses your job? Can one of the incomes handle the payments for several months? Have you considered the extra expenses that come with owning a house? Have you planned for some major purchases you are almost certain to need to make soon after buying a home - like lawn equipment, appliances, and furniture. What about moving expenses? And you may also have to shell out for closing fees, property taxes, and other financing expenses. And don't forget, your family may grow, creating new expenses.

Look, also, at the long haul. Buying a fabulous house may seem worth sacrifices right now, but after a year or two, will you feel deprived and unhappy when you can't afford a dinner out or a vacation?

Answer these questions honestly. Then sit down and decide for yourself how much of your income you really want to commit to housing. Don't just trust your lending institution to tell you what you can afford to pay - they don't live at your house, they don't know your special circumstances.

When you begin shopping for a house, it is a good idea to look only at those within the price range you decided on. If you look at the more expensive ones, you may be tempted to throw all caution to the winds and get yourself into a situation that is unbearable to you - and, remember, the mortgage will be hanging over your head for years.

Look into assumable mortgages. This is simply a situation where you take over the payments for someone else's home loan. When someone has owned a house for a relatively short period of time and then decides to sell, sometimes you can buy on an assumable mortgage. This type of purchase can work out well. What happens is: When you decide to buy the home, you pay the owners the down payment. Then you just take over their loan and make the payments. Of course, it isn't quite that simple, but that's pretty much what happens. You will have to work with their lending institution or with someone who can represent your interests to make the arrangements legal. DO NOT HAND OVER THE DOWN PAYMENT UNTIL LEGAL ARRANGEMENTS HAVE BEEN MADE. This can be a good way to buy a home. It is possible that their payments and their interest will be quite a bit lower than a new loan could be arranged at.

On the other hand, it is possible that the required down payment would be very large. But it might not be much larger than a regular down payment. It would depend on the circumstances of their loan and how badly they want to sell. Most likely they will want to get back what they have paid on the house. But if they figure the tax deductions they have had for the interest portion of their payments, they may not have actually paid out very much - the payments at the beginning of payback are mostly interest and very little principal.

It is worth looking at homes that you can buy on these assumable mortgages. You might find one with a down payment you can live with and get lower payments and interest than you expected.

Don't eliminate auctions. Some houses are offered for sale by auction. Sometimes you can save thousands of dollars when you buy this way. Be sure to visit your banker or lending institution to establish loan limits and get their advice before you bid on a house offered on auction.

After shopping for a home and talking to lenders, sellers, and real estate people for a while, it is easy to begin to think of interest in terms of percentages and points instead of dollars. But those percentages translate into dollars! You bet they do! Thousands of dollars that you have to shell out over the next many years. The following charts show you just how many dollars interest can add up to over a thirty year mortgage. They also show you how you can save thousands of dollars in interest over that period of time.

Save on Your Grocery Bill and Eat Better!

You can save money on your grocery bill, and since this is a regular expenditure, the savings can add up to a considerable amount over a year. All that is necessary to accomplish these savings is to become an informed and aware shopper.

One important fact to remember is that the grocer is in the business to make money. This can either work for or against you. As an informed shopper you can make it work for you.

Grocery stores buy some items on discount (on sale) from their suppliers. They pass these discounts on to you in the form of advertised specials or unadvertised in-store specials. The biggest discounts are usually BUT NOT ALWAYS the advertised specials. NEVER assume an advertised item, an impressively displayed item, or an item with a special sign on it is your best buy. These could be well-discounted items, but they may be marked down only a few cents or not marked down at all. Sometimes the big displays are items that the grocer can make a good profit from.

Grocers often use "leader" items in their ads. These are items that are extremely low priced, sometimes below the stores cost. Why do they sell below cost? Because these items are used to "lead you" into the store. They hope that once you are in the store you will purchase many items including some from the pretty displays that are only slightly discounted and, of course, regular shelf items that are not discounted at all.

This is normal business procedure and the grocer must, of course, attempt to make a profit. But it is your business to save as much as possible, so make the leader items work for you. First determine your need for the item. Strangely some people will purchase a bargain even though they will never use it. It is no bargain at any price if you'll never use it! Next check to see if the grocer is limiting purchases of the item. If allowed, purchase in large quantity, assuming, of course, that you can properly store it and will consume it before it expires.

Once you've been "led in," don't purchase everything in sight. You can be a smart shopper if you keep some of the following in mind.

Compare specially priced items against the price of "house brands." House brands are bargain brands that carry brand names unique to a particular supplying warehouse chain. Sometimes a store will have two or three house brands. Usually the packaging isn't as pretty as the national brands, but often the product is comparable in quality and priced considerably lower. Try them. If your family likes them, you have just found products that may be cheaper than national brands EVEN WHEN THE NATIONAL BRANDS ARE ON SALE. When house brands are offered at a special price they become exceptional values. Why pay extra for a pretty package or a well-advertised brand name?

But be careful - not all bargain brands are a bargain.
(a) Bargain brand bathroom tissue can sometimes be of such poor quality that it is necessary to use more so it doesn't last as long and, therefore, may cost more to use than a national brand.
(b) Bargain brand facial tissue, on the other hand, can be a real bargain since they are usually used once and tossed so the quality isn't very important. But be sure to check the number of sheets in the box.
(c) Paper toweling - for general use bargain brands can be a good buy. For sloppy clean-ups or wet cleaning, you may find an expensive brand will go further. Would it be wise for you to keep a roll of the more expensive towels for special use and a bargain brand in the towel holder for general use?
(d) Garbage bags - most bargain brand bags are of reasonable quality, but some are not. Certainly the small waste basket liners and tall kitchen liners should be satisfactory unless you have unusually heavy items in your trash. Some of the bargain brand large trash can liners may not be satisfactory, but it would be wise to try some of them. There is usually a considerable difference in price. Remember, "frills" such as drawstring tops and handle ties are expensive. Decide if these conveniences are that important.
(e) Health and beauty aids - tremendous savings can be gained by using house or bargain brands. Check labels for ingredients - often vitamins, pain relievers, and cold and flu remedies are priced dollars below comparable national brands.
(f) Pet foods - check the ingredient label for protein content - if that is satisfactory and your pet is satisfied with the taste, why pay dollars more for a well-known name?
(g) Detergents, soaps, cleaning aids - here again an area where you can save dollars by buying the house or bargain brand items. Most are satisfactory products. Try them.
(h) Other non-food products - light bulbs, napkins, paper plates and cups, diapers - Again, compare the house brands for quality and

price. You will find considerable savings on these products.

(i) Butter - house brand butter is often very good. You will likely have to forego the convenience of quarters since house brands are usually sold in unquartered one-pound blocks. The packaging is often poor, but the pricing is usually much lower than national brands. Try freezing butter. If satisfied with the results, you could take advantage of special prices by buying in quantity.

(j) Margarine - house brands are often inferior to national brands but may be ok for cooking and baking. Some of the medium- priced brands are reasonably good. You may want to try some of them. Again, try freezing for storing in quantity.

(k) Baking items such as sugar, syrup, cocoa, flour, shortening , and spices - house brands are often indistinguishable from national brands. In baking, you often get the same results from house brand ingredients as you do from national brand products. Any quality difference is seldom noticed in the baked item.

(l) Cereals - here house brands are almost always a real value. Quality is usually very good. The popular brand "kid cereals" are usually priced far above their nutritional value. The manufacturer and the grocery rely on the child's influence rather than value to sell these products. (Notice they are usually displayed at a shelf level that is convenient for children to see, and the box designs are appealing to children.) If you decide to buy a house brand nutritional cereal, you will save a considerable amount and have they added satisfaction of providing your child with better nutrition. Attractive packaging and highly advertised names are a very big factor in the pricing of cereals.

House or bargain brands are available in nearly every section of the supermarket. Check them out. Often the house brands are exactly the same product in different packaging. The reason for this is that often the national brand producer is also the house brand producer. Pretty packaging with a lot of colors is expensive. House brands usually use cheaper packaging and fewer colors.   Often the packaging is the ONLY difference between the expensive brand and the house brand.

Another sales device that is regularly used is the coupon. There are two types of coupons available to you. The manufacturer's coupon, which is found in magazines, newspapers, and other mailings, and the in-ad coupon, which is found in the grocer's advertisement. The use of coupons is restricted but still can save you money. If you have checked out coupons recently, you will know that there are very few nickel and dime coupons anyhow. Most a worth quite a bit, some are worth a dollar or more.

Manufacturer's coupons - These are provided by the manufacturer to encourage you to try their product. Use them but don't let them lead you into buying items that you won't use. You need to check before using coupons. Would another brand, even without a coupon, be a better bargain? The ideal time to redeem a coupon is when the item is on sale. Then you really get a bargain! But please, use them only for the specified item and follow the rules. Don't ask your grocer to honor a coupon on the purchase of a different brand or different item. It is against the law to do that, and the grocery can be prosecuted for fraud.

In-ad coupons - Usually you can redeem these for exceptionally good buys. In-ad coupons are a way for the grocer to limit purchases of a "leader" item. (That's the advertised item that "leads" you into the store, remember?) If it specifies one coupon purchase per family, don't ask to redeem more than one. However, if you have a friend or neighbor who hasn't a use for that coupon, ask her to go in and purchase the item for you. The grocer put that coupon in the ad to "lead" people in. If your friend comes into the store, she will likely purchase some items for herself or, at least, see what the store has to offer. It's a fair deal - you will get the extra coupon item and the store gets a visit from your friend.

Signs sell. Grocers are very aware of this. Many people simply buy whatever has a sign hanging in front of it. This is not a good policy. Take the time to compare the price against other brands. The discount may be very small if there is a discount at all.

Eye level merchandising. People tend to be "lazy" so the convenient shelf levels are often used for higher profit items. Check the less convenient (both lower and higher) shelves. You may find better buys there.

End cap displays. These are displays at the ends of aisles. These are attention getters. Check out these prices. Sometimes you will find really good buys here. Often, though, these are highly popular items with minimal discounts. Often, too, displays are built a day or two before the item is actually marked down. It is amazing how many of the items are purchased before the item is marked down at all!

Impulse items. These are items you hadn't intended to buy and, when you get home, wonder why you did. Usually they were so attractively and conveniently displayed that you just couldn't resist. Become aware of what makes you buy. When you know about the impulse items and can recognize them when you see them, it will be easier to resist them.

Mass merchandising. Mass merchandising is simply displaying merchandise in large quantity. Huge displays attract buyers. Sometimes it seems as though people are too polite to purchase the last item on the shelf, but when things are displayed in abundance they feel the need to buy more than they had planned to buy. Sometimes the items that are mass displayed are really very good bargains, and the mass display is simply to accommodate the large number of expected buyers. Sometimes, though, mass display is a planned method to urge people to buy more, and the discount may be minimal.

There is a certain psychology at work in the mass merchandising scheme that may also be at work in your home. So if you buy in large quantities to take advantage of bargain prices, it may be wise to store only small quantities conveniently close to the kitchen. Keep the rest in a storage area well away from the kitchen so you won't be tempted to use more than necessary at a time.

Another interesting grocery expense is the "entertainment spending." Often when people are buying groceries for picnics, cook-outs, camping trips, fishing trips, or other fun meals, they drop their guard. Suddenly it is not grocery shopping. It is entertainment. Certainly these things are fun, but they don't need to be so costly. With a little bit of planning, most of the grocery needs for these events can be purchased with the same sensible approach as your regular shopping. Perhaps a little extravagance is justified, but it is not a good policy to spend as much for one day at the lake as you normally do for a whole week grocery bill. A few of those days can really skyrocket the annual grocery budget!

Holiday meals - There is no reason why these meals can't be a bargain from beginning to end. Grocers become extremely competitive around holidays. If you begin watching the ads and planning you meal a week or two before the holiday, you should be able to pick up nearly every item you need on sale at one store or another. (This is also a good time to buy some items in quantity at holiday "leader" prices.) Watch the prices closely. Some stores will have some very good holiday prices on certain items but give you only small discounts on others.

Fresh produce is a department where you would rarely want to take advantage of the specials by buying in large quantities unless you will be freezing or canning the product. But you can save by buying produce in season when the price should be relatively low. Sometimes you can also save by buying smaller, less attractive produce. These items can be of equal quality. It's kind of like the cereal - you pay extra for the attractive "package."

Some produce hints to take advantage of good prices: Try washing seedless grapes and freezing in single layers. When partially thawed these make a sweet, delicious, and nutritious snack food. Sometimes stores will offer over-ripened bananas for just a few cents per pound. These can be mashed and measured out for your favorite recipes and then frozen until you are ready to use them for baking. Just thaw to use. Also, bananas will keep longer in the refrigerator. The peel turns dark but the fruit inside keeps longer. To ripen most fruit, just put it in a paper bag at room temperature. Leaving fruit in its packaging when you bring it home also speeds up the ripening process which results in quicker spoilage.

Convenience foods - this term includes everything from the tv dinner to the instant potatoes to the deli's ready-to-eat fare. There may be exceptions, but the general rule is "the closer to the mouth, the higher the price." Those handy little convenience items may be inflating your grocery bill. Can you make your own noodle or potato or rice side dish? Is a frozen pizza worth the extra cost or would a box pizza mix work as well? Can you make you own salad cheaper than the cost of a deli salad? These are questions you should consider. Maybe purchasing these kind of items has become a habit you haven't thought about. Maybe convenience foods are vital to your way of life and therefore are worth the extra cost.

Meats - In this department big savings are possible by buying in quantity when items are on sale. This is an area where a look at the price per portion is just as important as the price per pound. Sometimes what looks like a really expensive price per pound works out to a fairly reasonable price per serving. If you decide to buy an advertised item in a very large quantity, contact the store early in the week, let them know how much you want and how you want it cut and packaged. Often, a store will freezer wrap it in convenient packages (for instance two or three chops per package) at little or no extra cost. You may find that purchasing meat in quantity as it comes on sale is a better buy than purchasing a side or quarter, and you have the added advantage of purchasing only your favorite cuts. You may also find that leaner meats may be a better buy (as well as healthier) because there is less waste, and therefore more usable product, per pound. If you buy wieners, ground beef, chicken, or steak in quantity when on sale, you will have it on hand for that trip to the lake that might otherwise blow the grocery budget.

Soft drinks - seem to have become an almost essential item on the modern grocery list. The lack of nutritional value aside, the cost can become very substantial for the quantities many families consume. Luckily, there seems to be hardly a week when soft drinks of one brand or another are not on sale. This is a highly competitive item, especially in the twelve or larger pack. With a little planning, it shouldn't be necessary to ever purchase them at regular price. Watch the ads. Also check the bargain brands. These are often exceptionally reasonable and the quality is usually good. Soft drinks should not be refrigerated in quantity at home. If a cold can is always readily available, you will use far more. It would be a good idea to use aid drinks at least some of the time instead of canned soft drinks. The price per serving is more reasonable.

Bread - Breads can be frozen if you wish to buy in quantity. If you have a "day-old bakery outlet near you, you can get some real deals on bread. This bread actually freezes better than the really fresh bread does. Frozen bread works well for toast. Buying day-old bread to freeze in quantity is a good idea if you use a lot of toast, grilled sandwiches, and french toast. Day-old rolls are good after a quick warming in the microwave.

If you use a lot of an item that never seems to be run on sale, ask about a case discount. Many stores will give a discount of around 10% on case purchases because a case purchase saves handling (no unpacking and no stocking it to the shelf). However, if you can buy an item on sale, you usually get a better discount than you do for case pricing.

You may feel your budget can't afford quantity purchasing. In this case, I would recommend gradually working into it. Each week pick out an item or two that appeals to you and is an extremely good buy. Purchase a case or two. This would be a good method even if your budget is more flexible since you will then take advantage of only the very best bargains. Eventually you will have enough product on hand so that you will rarely need to purchase anything that is not on sale. Be careful. Don't over-buy perishables. Determine how much of a certain product you can store properly and use before it expires.

Watch prices. The "hot" advertised leader prices may create a low-priced image when, in fact, another store with less "hot" advertised Also, don't rule out the small stores. A smaller store may yield some unexpected bargains.

And finally, the old but very good advice. Don't shop when you are hungry. When you are hungry, everything looks good and impulse buying is harder to control. You tend to buy expensive ready-to-eat items.

Often the nutritionally poor foods are among both the most expensive and the most purchased items in the store. As an informed and careful shopper, you CAN eat better for much less cost.

Houseware and Hardware Bargains

Are you paying regular list price for most of the items you buy? Or do shop the sales and think you are getting a great buy? Maybe you are finding great bargains - but maybe you could do better. Maybe you could buy tools, toys, housewares, and even larger items for far less than you are paying even when you buy things on sale.

If you want to save really big bucks, you'll have to do more than run down to the store when they advertise a sale. Of course, there is nothing wrong with doing that - sometimes you do find a real bargain there, too. You have to be careful, though. Sale items at a store sometimes are not such great bargains as they appear to be - often they use second rate merchandise for advertised items. Sometimes they deliberately advertise second-rate or stripped down versions of the items just to get you into the store. When you get there, they are not very interested in selling the item to you. In fact, sometimes they will tell you, "oh, that item didn't come in because of shortages (or shipping problems or some other lame excuse)." And then what do they say? "But, we just happen to have a better model at just a slightly higher price. Let me show it to you." Right. They've suckered you into the store with the advertised item and now will try to sell you a different version. By this time, you've probably got your heart set on buying the item so you figure, "What the heck, this one isn't THAT much more and look at all the extra features the salesman says I'll get." So you buy it and take it home thinking you got a real bargain. But is it a bargain? Probably not.

But, as we said, sometimes an advertised special at a store is a real bargain, so it is wise to continue to check them out. However, it is not wise to limit yourself to that one type of bargain hunting. There are a lot of other ways to purchase the items you need at a fraction of the regular retail price.

Check out garage sales and moving sales. Of course, the merchandise you find here is used, but often that doesn't really matter. If you are in the need of something like tools, for instance, does it really make a difference if they are not new? If they are in perfectly good condition and a good brand name and you can buy a $22 item for just a couple of bucks, you've just found yourself a terrific bargain. You can find similar deals on toys - especially big ticket items like swing sets and bicycles. As far as household items, sometimes this is THE place to find unique, antique items that you couldn't find at ANY price in a store.

But even at garage sale prices, you can sometimes do better than the asking price. Don't be afraid to offer a lower price. The owners are selling these things because they want to get rid of them - they are running out of storage space, moving, or need the money - so they may be very willing to come down on their prices. Another trick to garage sale purchasing is to come back towards the end of the last day of the sale. If the items you want aren't sold by then, the owner is likely to be receptive to a very low offer.

Estate sales are another source of real bargains. At these sales, the family or the administrator of the estate does the pricing. Because the property was not purchased or held by these people, they do not always know the value of certain items. Another thing that works in your favor is that they are usually anxious to get rid of the items and turn them into cash. You can pick up some great bargains at these sales.

Auction sales are also good sources of true bargains. Here the items are not priced by the owner but go to the highest bidder so, in reality, the bidding crowd sets the prices. With the right crowd, some items are virtually given away. If the bidding seems to be setting the prices high at a particular sale, don't give up. Usually some items will still go for really low prices. Be careful, though. Just as some bidding crowds will set lower prices and some will set higher prices, they can also set moods. Be careful not to get caught up in the excitement that some bidding crowds create. Sometimes people will end up paying more at an auction for used items than they would have paid at regular retail for the same items new! But you will be amazed at what you can buy at auction sales for very low prices. Would you believe even cars and houses?

On items like cars and houses you can save thousands of dollars. Houses? At auction sales? Yes, and it isn't just private owners who are selling houses by auction. Government agencies and banks do, too. These are houses that become available through foreclosures or things like the savings and loan failures or the liquidation of estates. Watch your newspapers for advertisements. There is a procedure you must follow for purchasing a house by auction. Go to your bank before you go to the auction. You will need to talk about financing and determine what your mortgage limits are. The bank needs to be in on your plans, if you intend to get a loan from them to pay for the house. Once you have the bank approval, go for it! But go with caution - a house isn't a bargain if it isn't right for you. Be sure to check it out before you bid on it, and know the value of the property before you bid on it. Remember bidding is like making an offer. Don't offer more than the house is worth or more than your loan approval. With cautious shopping, you may be able to save thousands - up to 25 or 30 percent!

For cars, check out police auctions. At these sales, police offer seized and abandoned property. You can find real bargains here - save up to one-half of what you'd expect to pay at a used-car lot. Be sure to go and look them over before you buy. If you don't know much about cars, take someone along who does. You don't want to pay too much simply because you don't know the value of the car. Police auctions don't deal with financing so go prepared. You usually have to bring cash or a certified check with you and pay at the time of purchase.

If you would prefer to buy new items, look for liquidation auctions. Sometimes these are held right at the firms that is being liquidated. Other times liquidations are handled differently. Professional liquidators may purchase the entire stock to be liquidated. These people may also purchase surplus or liquidation stock from other firms before holding an auction. So liquidation auctions can offer a variety of toys, housewares, furniture, tools, and other items. At these auctions you can find some real bargains on unused items. As at any auction, you must exercise caution. Inspect the merchandise beforehand, if possible. And be wary of bidding-crowd behavior. Always know the value of the item you are bidding on. Remember, auction prices are not always bargains.

Car Performance

Do you feel that cars just don't last very long? Does it seem that every time you turn around you are either having major repairs done on your car or that you are in need of a different car?

Although we get disgusted when we have trouble with our vehicles, they are a complicated bunch of moving parts that take an awful beating. We really can't expect them to last forever, but we can do some things to keep them at a good performance level for a long time.

How? Well, we must give them a lot of attention. Like people, they need regular check-ups. This is not free, of course. But the time and money you put into maintaining your car will pay off in the many more miles it will last before you need to replace it.

Just taking it into a garage and telling them to look it over probably isn't going to do the trick. You need to tell them what you want checked and what you want done. Probably your most important tool will be a notebook or chart on which you keep a maintenance record. Another tool you should have in your possession is a copy of your owner's manual.

You probably already have the oil checked regularly - it's a good idea to have this done every time you fill up the gas tank - and changed periodically. That's good. It's very important to the life of your car.

The reason you need to change oil periodically is that it collects particles of metal and dirt and other abrasives that can accumulate and wreck your engine. This accumulation is what the mechanics see when they tell you your oil is dirty. If you let it go too long without changing it, a good service man can tell by the color of the oil on the dipstick when he checks your oil. So changing the oil is a matter of draining out the dirty oil and putting in clean. Check your owner's manual to see how often the manufacturer recommends you change the oil. Use the recommendation as a guide - but if you drive on dusty roads, live in a cold climate, or make a lot of short trips, you should change it more often than the manufacturer recommends. It won't damage your car if you change the oil a little too often, but changing it too seldom can cause real problems. The oil filter needs to be replaced periodically, too. Check your owner's manual to see how frequently your vehicle's manufacturer recommends changes.

The type of oil you use in your car can make a big difference in the life of your engine, too. Use a good quality oil and one that is suitable for the climate you live in.

When you have your oil changed, you should ask the mechanic to examine the underside of the car. Ask him to check for any leakage from the radiator, engine, differential, transmission, and wheels. Have him look at the steering system and the exhaust system while he's under it. Catching any problems while they are still minor will help you avoid big problems. Look in your owner's manual - if your car needs lubrication with every oil change, ask the mechanic to do that, too. Make sure he checks the fluid levels while you have it in the shop. Don't forget to jot down what services you have had done along with the date and the mileage reading.

Every automobile engine needs a tune-up regularly. In addition to lengthening its life, a tune-up will increase your engine's gas mileage and improve the way it runs and starts. Now, a good tune-up should include your entire engine system, and while you have your car in the shop, you should have the mechanic check other things, as well. Actually your engine system consists of several systems working together. Each of these systems needs attention during the tune-up. Let's step through what needs to be done.

Did you know that your engine breathes? It even has a breather tube! You will want to make sure that this breathing system is checked.   In fact, a compression test should be the first test run during your tune-up.   This test can reveal problems that the mechanic should be aware of before he begins the tune-up of the other systems.

The spark plugs are removed to do the compression test. Your plugs should be examined. Your plugs make a big difference in how smoothly your car runs, how well it accelerates, and its gas mileage. Plugs can wear or collect dirt, moisture, or other deposits. Sometimes they just need cleaning;   sometimes they need replacing.

Your mechanic should also do a vacuum test. This test will reveal problems with the valves, ignition, timing, and manifold.

Your mechanic should take a look at your ignition system. Be sure he checks out the battery and plug cables and wires as well as the mechanical components of the system.

The fuel system also needs attention. Your fuel tank, of course, is a part of this system. You should check this occasionally for leaks. Or you can ask your mechanic to check it.   Your mechanic should check the fuel pump volume, pressure, and vacuum and clean or replace your fuel filter. The carburetor is very complex and should be checked out thoroughly. It determines fuel mixture which affects how smoothly your car will run and its gas mileage.   There are several components in the carburetor which need to be tested and checked.

The air cleaner needs attention, too. The air filter will probably need to be cleaned or replaced. A dirty or damaged are filter permits dust and dirt to pass through causing wear on the engine. Even if the damage appears to be very tiny, the filter should be replaced.

Your emission control devices or system should be checked to see that it is working properly and not damaged.

Most of the attention to the starting system will be focused on your battery, but the leads and switches should be checked, too. Your mechanic should inspect the wires and cables for loose connections, damaged wires, and frayed insulation. He should tighten all connections that are loose.   The battery should be cleaned - dirt and corrosion around the posts will allow current leakage. Corrosion can build up between the posts and the cable terminals, too. This build-up can interfere with proper electrical contact. Both the posts and the cable terminals should be cleaned.

The battery is also a part of the electrical system of your car. This system also consists of an alternator, regulator, and wiring. Your mechanic should inspect the alternator and regulator. He should also scan the wiring securing any loose wires.

Ask your mechanic to check the cooling system for leaks. The coolant level should be checked, and if necessary, it should be drained and refilled. The front of the radiator should be cleaned of bugs and dirt so it will operate more efficiently. Your mechanic should check all hose clamps for tightness and inspect the hoses for brittleness, cracks, or bulging.

Have your mechanic check the exhaust system for corrosion, broken hangers, and loose clamps and connections. Have him also look at the brake system including the shock absorbers.

Ask him to take a look at your wheel balance and alignment. Have him take a quick look at the tires while he's at it.

Now this may seem like a lot of things to check - and it is - but most of the checking is not too difficult and will not take long. If you don't have every system checked, you can't be sure that your vehicle is operating at its best. With a complete check regularly, you'll find minor problems before they develop into big problems. Like people who should have a regular physical exam to ward off problems, your car needs a regular check-up. As we said, your car is a complicated bunch of moving parts. Each part is an integral part of the vehicle. Often, one part that isn't operating properly can affect other parts and/or the life of the vehicle.

How often should you schedule this extensive check-up? We would recommend that it be done once a year for most vehicles. If you drive your vehicle more than ordinary or drive it hard, you may want to have it done more often. Scheduling the extensive check-up for the fall of the year is a good idea, especially if you live where the winters are cold. You should also have a check done in the spring, though it needn't be quite so extensive.

Of course, you may need to do some maintenance more often. For instance, you will want to change your oil at least as often as your owner's manual suggests. You should check your coolant level about every month. During the summer you should check your radiator for dirt and bug build-up and clean it whenever necessary. Check your battery periodically for corrosion build up. You should get into the habit of visually checking your tires whenever you are walking up to your car. Check the air level in your tires regularly.

Also get into the habit of listening to your engine run. When you do this as a habit, you will notice when it's "running funny". Have it checked as soon as possible if you notice anything different. If it's misfiring get it fixed promptly to avoid damage.

Your style of driving can also affect your car's performance. Often, we develop driving patterns that we are not even aware of. Monitor yourself and watch for fast starts, heavy braking or riding the brake, and high speeds.

If you are like most people, you are very dependent on your car. It only makes sense to keep it at its peak performance. A good regular maintenance program and sensible driving habits will keep it at its best and extend the life of the vehicle, as well.

Repair

Do you sometimes feel the cost of repairing things is more expensive than just replacing them? Yet here you are, caught in a dilemma. If you replace something with a new item, how long will it be before you will be needing expensive repairs on it? Mechanical items seem to have perverse personalities. They know when any warranty or guarantee expires! Almost to the day! Well, of course, it's foolish to assign a personality and a thought process to inanimate objects, but doesn't it seem like they know and plan for the day the warranty expires? Then, too, if you decide to replace the item, there is the major problem of disposing of the old one. Sometimes that is an expensive proposition, too. And then most of us are also conscious of the conservation side of the issue and want to get the most use we can of an article before tossing it out. So, what can you do to hold those repair bills down?

A goodly portion of the money you spend on repairs probably goes into fixing your automobile. Repairs and maintenance on an automobile can add up fast. Now there is a difference between repairs and maintenance. Both cost money, it's true, but your maintenance dollars can save a lot of repair dollars. Be sure you keep a regular maintenance schedule - check and change your oil regularly, check the fluids often, keep your tires properly inflated and aligned, get regular grease jobs. Keeping your car well maintained will avoid unnecessary stress on it. Your repair bills will be less.

But eventually you will need repairs on the vehicle. Every time you take your car in for repairs or even for maintenance, you are at risk of being ripped off. Even a little maintenance like checking the oil can be a rip-off. If the oil stick is pushed is just part of the way when it is checked, it will show that your oil is low. So when you are shown the oil stick as proof that you need to buy oil, it could be a rip-off. Now, some mechanics are very good and scrupulously honest, but some are not. The ones who are not can cost you a bundle. But you can avoid some of the unnecessary costs.

You need to be aware of some of the tricks dishonest mechanics pull. The transmission is probably the most common problem area for rip-offs. It's complicated so most people don't know much about them. Dishonest mechanics know this and take advantage of it. Probably the easiest rip-off trick - and the most common - is pointing out metal filings in the transmission pan as proof that your transmission is badly in need of repair or replacement. Don't believe it! If it is just shavings and not chunks or pieces, you're OK. It's just normal wear. Keep an eye on the mechanic while he is removing the pan. He may plant some chunks in it.

He might try other tricks, too - like spraying oil on the engine or other parts so that there appears to be a leak of oil or other fluids. He might tell you that this leak means that you need to replace or repair a major part.

Be wary of the suggestion that there are multiple parts that need to be replaced to take care of a problem you are having with your car. Of course, it's possible that more than one thing needs to be replaced, but it's more possible that the problem stems from a single source.

Don't leave the car for repairs without getting a copy of the work order. You may find a huge bill for other repairs that he did "while he was in there." It is easy for a dishonest mechanic to make a few extra bucks by replacing a couple of other parts as long as he has the car in the shop and on the hoist.

The really overtly dishonest mechanic may try something like puncturing your tire or cutting your fan belt, too.

These are only a few of the tricks that are pulled on unsuspecting motorists every day. The list could go on and on. So how can you protect yourself from these rip-offs?

Well, knowing how the dishonest mechanic operates helps. You can watch for his tricks. Keep an eye on what he's doing. Never leave your car in a shop without getting a copy of the work order. Never sign an "open-ended" work order - make sure the work order states specifically what the mechanic is to replace or repair.

If you know little or nothing about cars, bring someone along who does - or have that someone take the car into the shop for you. If you can talk to the mechanic like you know what is going on, he will be less likely to try to pull something. After all, he doesn't want to get caught at his tricks. It's especially important for women to either know about cars or send her car to the shop with someone else. Women are ripped off more often than men.

Like going to a doctor, you don't have to accept the mechanic's opinion of what needs to be done - you can seek a second opinion - and even a third. Don't be afraid to walk out of a shop that you feel is questionable.

Ask about a written estimate. Ask if they call before doing repairs that will cost more than the estimate. Ask if they will guarantee parts and labor in writing. Ask if they will give you the old parts that they remove from your car. Ask if the mechanic actually takes your car out for a test drive before he works on it so he can judge what is wrong with it. Ask if he takes for a test drive after he works on it to make sure the problem is taken care of.

Or find a diagnostic center that doesn't do repair work. If they don't actually do the repair work, they have no stake in suggesting unnecessary repairs.

Look for a mechanic you can trust and stick with him. How do you find him? Again like you do with doctors, ask for references. Ask people you know to recommend a mechanic. Ask anyone. Ask more than one person. Keep a record. Soon you will find that some get a lot of good recommendations, and some you get warnings about again and again. If you are traveling, and find you are in need of a mechanic, stop at a couple of businesses and ask the employees to recommend a shop. Most people honestly want to help visitors to their community and usually will be happy to advise you. Remember, too, that in addition to dishonest mechanics there are those who just don't know their job very well. He may not be intentionally ripping you off. He may be doing the best he can do. The incompetent mechanic can cost you a bundle, though he is certainly a more admirable person than the intentionally dishonest one. When you car needs attention, you need to avoid the nice guy who doesn't know his job, too.

When you find a good mechanic - one you can trust and who listens closely to you when you tell him about the symptoms you are concerned about - stick with him even if he charges a little more than others. In the end it will save you money. Low prices for repairs you don't need are no bargain.

Repairs to your home are also expensive. Especially if you are remodeling or building on an addition. Again you will have to deal with people who may be honest and talented, but could be incompetent and dishonest. To avoid problems, you should decide definitely what you want and be specific when you talk to the repairman. Don't leave him guessing. Even if he is honest, you may end up with something you don't want. If you don't tell him you want quality materials, he may think you want to get by as cheaply as possible and use lower-grade materials. On the other hand, you could want to get by as cheaply as possible, but he may assume you want quality and you could end up with a larger repair bill than you had planned for. Whether he is honest or not, specific instructions about what you want done, how you want it done, and what kind of materials you want could forestall problems.

If you aren't sure you can trust him, keep an eye on what he is doing. Check to make sure the materials are of the grade chosen by you. Check this throughout the job. If you know what materials are going into the job, you can avoid paying for a better quality than you actually got. If you don't check up on him, he could substitute a lower grade and charge you for quality grade materials

Make sure you have a specific work agreement or contract. It should be very specific about what is to be done, what materials will be used, what quality those materials will be, what the job will cost, and when the job will be completed. Yes, even when the job will be completed should be included.

A completion date is especially important if the job is a large one. Sometimes a contractor will take on more jobs than he can possibly complete in a satisfactory length of time. He will begin the job to have a hold on you. Then he will move on and begin another job and another. Soon he has several jobs in progress and will devote only an occasional day to each. He knows it's difficult to drop him and find someone else to do the job if he has begun the project. So be sure to have a specific completion date. This will discourage him from leaving you hanging for months with a half-completed project.

If you have repairmen coming into your home or on your property, be sure to have them give you proof that they are carrying liability insurance on the work they do. Also be sure they have liability and workman's compensation insurance. If you don't understand the papers they give you for proof of coverage or if you question the validity of them, get phone numbers of the insurance company and call them to verify the coverage. This is very important. If they are not covered by insurance, you could be held liable for any mishaps or accidents that occur while they are working on your property. That could really cost you a bundle.

Many of the common rip-offs can be avoided by being aware of the tricks that can be pulled, by being careful in choosing your repairmen, and by knowing something about the repairs yourself. However, if you feel that you have been ripped off, don't hesitate to report it.

You have a lot of options available to you if you have been ripped off. Call or write your local or state consumer-protection agency. Include as much documentation as possible - copies of work-orders, estimates, contracts, bills, cancelled checks, whatever paper work you have. Or contact your district attorney or state attorney-general. Talk to the Better Business Bureau. Some states have offices that deal specifically with car repair complaints - find out if yours does. If the shop you are having problems with is affiliated with a national chain, write to the parent company. Use your small claims court. Use these options. You don't have to sit back and take it when you think you've been ripped off.

Utility Bills

Are your utility bills out of hand? If they are, you are not alone. Knowing a lot of families have the same problem may be of some comfort. It does not, however, save you any money.

What you need to know is how some people manage to control their utility costs. It can be done. There really are some conservation tricks that can save you a lot of money.

You can save money on your water bills and your water heating bills by simply repairing any leaking faucet's. It may seem that a little drip-drip is merely annoying but it is also costly. Once the faucet's are all repaired, make sure the kids know how to shut them off completely and that they do it.

Most toilets use far more water than is necessary to flush. With a minor adjustment, you can set the amount of water used for flushing to the level you want. Just lift the lid of the tank. In the tank, you will usually find a float. This is the ball-like thing that floats to the top of the water as the tank fills. It is also the apparatus that determines how full the tank will get. Adjust the float to the water level that you want. It is simple, and with a little experimenting you will have it mastered. Saving a couple of gallons for each flush saves a lot of gallons per month. Think how many times the toilet is flushed each day, then think how many times each month. It really adds up, doesn't it?

Do you set out the sprinkler and water your grass and garden for hours at a time? Most people water their lawns, trees, and plants far more than needed. A healthy lawn and garden can usually be achieved with a half or even a third of the water most people use. If you cut back a little at a time, you can easily find the proper amount of watering for your lawn without damaging it. If you find you have water running down the street when you water, you can cut back considerably — you are watering too much.

Check out your water heater. Fifteen to twenty-five percent of your utility bill is probably for hot water. This is not a small percentage so making some changes here could cut your utility bills considerably. If your water heater is an old clunker, it is likely using more electricity or gas than it should. New water heaters are more efficient. The cost of replacing the clunker could easily be made up in lower utility bills. When you purchase a new one, make sure it is well insulated. If you are stuck with a poorly insulated or clunker water heater, wrap it with an insulation blanket (after you determine this would not be a fire hazard.) Insulate the hot-water pipes, too. Put a timer on your water heater. If no one is home during certain hours why maintain hot-water temperatures during those times? Set the heaters temperature lower - 20 or even 40 degrees lower probably will make no real difference since you almost always use a hot/cold mix anyway. For each 20 degree reduction in temperature, you will save 25 - 30 percent on your water heating bill. If you use a dishwasher, however, be sure to keep the water heater set at a safe temperature for operating it (about 140 degrees).

Assess your lighting habits. It is not necessary to have lights on in the entire house. Light only those rooms that are occupied. Do you have automatic lights that come on in the evening and shut off in the morning? Is it necessary to have them burning all night? Perhaps you should install a manual switch so you can shut them off when they are not needed.

Fluorescent lights use less power than regular light bulbs. Adapters are available so you can use fluorescents in regular light bulb sockets. The fluorescent bulbs come in a variety of sizes and shapes, so even many decorator lamps can be converted from regular bulbs to fluorescent bulbs. Look at changing your large wattage bulbs with smaller wattage bulbs. Some types of bulbs actually give less than other types of the same wattage. Look for reflector bulbs and clear bulbs. When you use these, you can use a smaller wattage and still get the same amount of light.

Resetting your thermostat can save you money. During the heating season, setting the temperature just a few degrees lower will probably not even be noticed but can save you money. Putting it on an automatic timer to lower the temperature when no one is at home or at night when no one is up and about will also be a big saving on your utility bill. If you can with the system you have, put thermostats in each room or area. This will allow you to cut the temperature in unused areas such as porches, halls, and spare bedrooms. You probably know that the warmest air in a room is near the ceiling. A ceiling fan can bring this air down. Run it at its lowest setting.

If your furnace is an older model, consider replacing it or at least making modifications and adjustments. Replacing your old furnace can save you a bundle in utility bills. Old furnaces are usually inefficient. What this means is that a large percentage of the heat is just plain going up the chimney. So check out that old furnace of yours! If you feel you don't want to change your furnace at this time, get a furnace man in to look at modifying or adjusting it. There are several fairly inexpensive things he can do to make your furnace more efficient. Your investment in these repairs will result in lower utility bills and should pay for themselves in a short time.

Many of the points made for heating units are true for the air conditioning unit. During cooling season, reset your units thermostat a few degrees lower. If your air conditioning unit is older, look at replacing it. It may be inefficient. Sometimes it wouldn't even be necessary to run your air conditioner at all if the windows are opened for the coolness at night and closed against the heat of the day. Pulling drapes and shades during the day helps to keep the heat out. Using awnings, jalousies, blinds, and sun reflecting storm windows also helps. If your air conditioner is older, it may be inefficient. Look at replacing it with a new efficient model.

Checking the insulation factor of your house is important, too. Maybe you need to re-insulate the entire house, maybe just an extra layer of insulation in the attic will do the trick. Attic insulation is usually a fairly easy procedure. All you need do is lay the insulating mats or a few inches of loose insulation over the insulation that is already there. Check the basement and crawl spaces. You may need to seal the crack between the house and the foundation. Staple insulation mats to the underside of the flooring above crawl spaces. On the walls and ceilings of unheated basements nail furring strips to allow you to insert insulation mats, which can then be covered with wallboard or paneling. Properly insulated homes are much cheaper to heat and to cool.

Check your house for air leaks to caulk or weatherstrip. Check around doors and windows and check your electrical wall sockets. Check existing caulking and weatherstripping to see if it needs to be replaced. After the weather is cold, check by running your hand over the areas. You will easily find your problem areas then! Patch the leaks you find.

Make sure you use your storm windows. If you don't have storm windows for some of your windows, the purchase will soon pay for itself in lower utility bills. Resort to the taped on "plastic sheet storm window," if you are unable to purchase regular storm windows right now. They aren't as effective as the regular storm windows, but they will help to reduce cold air infiltration.

Fixing the leaks around your doors may be only half the job in that area. You will want to check the KIND OF DOORS you have, too. If you have hollow-core outside doors, you will want to replace them with solid wood or insulated metal doors.

Check your major appliances. If they are old, they may be very inefficient. Newer appliances are more energy efficient. Check your motors. Yes, motors - make sure they are cleaned and oiled. At the same time, you should check your refrigerator vent, furnace filter, air-conditioner filter. If things are not cleaned and oiled regularly, your utility bills will be higher.

By just being aware of excesses and problem areas and then practicing easy conservation techniques, you can save a considerable amount of money on your utility bills.

Credit

Credit is a part of your life. Whether a good part or bad part depends a great deal on what you use it for and what your personal credit rating is.

Credit is fairly easy to get once you have established a good credit rating. Probably too easy. It can get you into a jam - a situation where you owe more than you can easily pay off and/or your payments become a burden.

However, without credit, most of us would be unable to buy a home or a car. Credit cards and charge accounts make purchasing the things we need or want easier. And credit is a very handy thing to have in an emergency. Yes, credit is an important part of modern living.

It is very important to establish yourself as credit worthy. It may even be a good idea to take a fairly small loan that you don't really need just to establish your credit. Be sure to make your payments on time - just getting a first loan will not establish your credit unless you follow through with regular payments.

Establishing credit can be rather difficult. If you are applying for a loan for the first time, you may find it a difficult thing to do. Even if you have a good job and a decent income you may run into problems when attempting to obtain a first loan. And without that first loan, how can you get a second loan?

What can you do?

Prepare yourself for the loan interview. You will have to get your act together. You should bring some of your financial papers with you. Have them organized! Your lender may not need to see everything you bring but you should be prepared. We suggest the following:

Your last income tax return, your credit card numbers and balances, statements pertaining to any investments you may hold, a statement of your personal worth (a list of what you own and what you owe), a budget that shows your monthly income and your expenses and payments - showing how you intend to make the payments on this loan, and your resume.

Don't just walk in unannounced - make an appointment beforehand and be on time. Be prepared to discuss your reasons for wanting the loan and be specific about how much you need and why. Be organized and confident in the manner in which you present your records and information. Handle it much like a job interview - be neat in your appearance. As in a job interview, you are selling yourself.

Even with this preparation you are not guaranteed to get a loan, but you will have a better chance. If you are turned down, don't worry about it - turn-downs don't go on your credit history. And don't get discouraged. Keep trying - it's important to get that first loan to establish a credit history.

You may find that it is easier to establish your credit history with smaller things first. If you buy a car on credit, for instance, the car itself becomes most, if not all, of the collateral you need for that loan. Or try borrowing against your savings account or certificates of deposit. It is easier to get a loan that is completely secured. A secured loan is one where you put up collateral - borrow against something - like a savings account or car. When you do that, the lending institution can take the collateral if you don't make the payments. Your lender certainly doesn't want the property - they'd much rather get the payments - but this type of loan reduces their risk. They can take the collateral and sell it to get the money back. This is not to say that secured loan are a snap - you will still need to be prepared for the loan interview.

A savings account can be a help in another way when applying for a loan. It shows that you have the discipline and/or sufficient income to cover your expenses and live on less than you earn. It's also important that you keep your checking account "clean" - no overdrafts. When you want a loan, your lender will look at your financial history - which includes your checking account.

Charge accounts that you make regular and timely payments on are also helpful credit history. It is a good idea to establish some charge accounts just so they become a part of your credit history. But you must make the payments on time! You want a good credit history.

Living in the same place for several years can also be a help. Somehow lenders look at this as a sign of stability. They also look at how long you have worked for the same employer. If you are moving around in jobs because of advancement in your career, be sure to point that out. Advancing is looked at with favor while just bouncing around in jobs is not.

It may become necessary to have someone co-sign for you. This is a matter of finding someone who has a good, established credit rating who will vouch for you. A co-signer is, in effect, promising to make the payments on your loan if you don't. Co-signing is not to be taken lightly - you are asking a very big favor of anyone who you ask to co-sign for you. You will not want to ask anyone who you are not on very familiar terms with. A parent may be a possible co-signer.

Where can you get a loan?

Your best bet is the financial institution where you do your business - where you have a checking account or savings account. Building and maintaining a financial relationship with an institution is a very good policy. If you have at least one financial institution that knows you and is involved in a lot of your financial business, it can be a great help to you later when you may need a large loan or when you have an emergency.

Do you have a credit union? Credit unions are a good place to get loans - you may find the best rates with them.

Do you have a savings account at a savings and loan? You may find their interest rates favorable.

Do you do your business at a bank? Try them for your loan. You may pay more interest than at your credit union or savings and loan, but a bank is a good financial institution to do business with - their multi-services could be of help in other areas of your financial life.

If you don't have any luck with the above institutions, try other banks and savings and loans. Although you should do better with the institutions where you do business, you might get lucky at one that you haven't done business with before.

Your last choice should be a finance company. It may be easier to get a loan from them, but be prepared to pay more interest - usually they charge a higher rate. Still, if you need a first loan to establish credit, it may be worth the extra interest.

If you are in a position to shop around for a loan, look for the best interest rate you can get. In comparing rates, compare the annual percentage rates. There is no need to pay more than you have to - unless you are attempting to build a financial relationship with a particular institution. Paying a little more may be worth the relationship you are building.

Credit cards are loans, too - though a little different. Credit cards are handy little things to have but can be the source of financial headaches. They should be handled with care. They are part of your financial history and regular payments on them can be of some help in establishing your worthiness for a bank loan.

To keep credit card spending under control, you should never spend more on a credit card than you can pay off within the grace period, unless it is an emergency. The grace period for most cards is twenty to thirty days - know the terms of your card! Find out what the billing cycle is and what the grace is. Pay off the balance every month within the grace period. In addition to helping to keep your credit spending under control, you'll be saving a bundle in interest - the interest rates are usually extremely high - rarely less than 14 percent and often over 20 percent! And the interest is not tax deductible. Besides all that, the timely payments will look good on you credit history.

Do you think all Visa and MasterCard cards are the same? Not! They vary depending on the state and even the bank where you got it. Don't depend on the information your friend has about a card - you need to check out yours. Not only the interest rates, but the annual fees can vary.

You've been offered a gold card or other premium card - is this good? Probably not. Although the interest rate may be the same, check out the monthly and annual fees. You may be paying a lot for the privilege of flashing that gold! Is it worth it? Only if you need an ego boost.

You've heard about credit card loans? These are the cash advances that many cards offer. These are very expensive loans - remember, the interest rates for most cards are very high. If you are going to do a credit card loan, look for a card with lower interest rates - none are low, but some are lower than others. Also, check out the interest break points. If you run up a large balance on one card, the interest may be lower than running up a smaller balance on two.

Once you have secured credit it's important to turn it into a good credit rating. It is not too difficult to figure out how that is done - just make your payments on time!

Problems may arise, however. Once you have established credit, it is easier to get credit - perhaps, too easy. This makes it easy to get in over your head. Be careful. Don't depend on the lender to determine how much debt you can handle! Just because you qualify for credit in the eyes of a lender, doesn't mean you can easily make the payments.

Prepare for financial difficulties. The best way to retain your good credit even through periods of financial difficulties is to communicate with your lender. Stop in and chat with your lender periodically. Show that you are in control of your financial affairs and concerned about maintaining your good credit. Don't be afraid of discussing your financial plans with your lender and asking her advice.

When you get into difficulties - like the loss of your job or an illness or major repairs to your car - be sure to talk to your lender BEFORE you get behind on your payments. Since you have been making your payments regularly, stopping in to talk with her periodically, and are immediately concerned about letting her know when you are having difficulties, she will know that you are concerned about your personal finances - and she will be more willing to work with you during your temporary difficulties and it will look better on your credit history.

Use your good credit wisely! Don't borrow for unnecessary things. Use it only for worthwhile things.

Buying a home is a good reason to borrow - if you plan wisely. You will want a nice home but don't go overboard. Remember, you will have to make those payments for a very long time. You may feel you are willing to give up a few things now to get that beautiful home, but will you be willing to forego those things for years? Don't let house payments put you in a position of never being able to take a vacation, for instance. Make sure you don't put yourself in a position of being so "house-poor" that you are in a financial bind every time some little unplanned thing comes up - like doctor or dental bills.

Improvements to your home are a good reason to borrow - as long as you can afford them and they truly add value to your home.

Education for your children is, of course, a good reason to borrow.

Borrowing to get you over unexpected financial emergencies is a good reason to borrow - it will help you keep your credit history clean.

Borrowing to buy a car is OK. You will want to be careful here, though, so that you don't buy a more expensive car than you can really afford. If you can't afford to pay it off in three years, you can't afford that car.

Borrowing to start a business is OK - as long as you can afford to invest a pretty good sum of your own and have enough for two or three months of operating costs and have at least enough money saved for three months of living expenses.

Borrowing for anything else is probably not a good idea, but whatever you borrow for keep those payments current. It is much easier to ruin your credit than it is to establish your credit. Just a few late payments will be a blot on your credit.

Make credit a good part of your life. Use your credit wisely and make you payments regularly - a good credit line is very handy in an emergency.

Safety Deposit Boxes

You may have valuables and a will that you don't want strangers to look over. Perhaps you have an idea of leaving a few thousand dollars for your family - a source of ready untaxable cash for them when you die.

You put your will, some cash, and other valuables in a safe deposit box at your bank. There everything is safe from prying eyes. Only you can get at them while you are living. Only the persons you designate can get at them when you die. Right? Wrong!

When you die, your safe deposit box could be sealed until authorities make an inventory of the contents. Your family may need permission and AUTHORITIES PRESENT to even open it for a will search! They may not be allowed to remove anything from the box until authorities have an opportunity to look over everything and record each item. This can create hassles for your family, not to mention that you have strangers pawing over your valuables. Many states require a special court procedure to open a safe deposit box for a will search. This could mean even more delays.

A safe deposit box is OK for stock certificates, life insurance policies, home deeds, and a copy of your will. It is not a place to keep your will, deed to cemetery plots, or cash.

It may be advisable to leave your will with your lawyer or family advisor. Or get a fire-proof safe to keep in your home. Be sure to check out the fireproofing. Some safes that claim to be fireproof could be less than adequate. A steel box is not fire-proof. Remember, when a house burns temperatures can get very hot! If the box doesn't burn but the papers inside turn into a curled, crisp, unreadable mess, of what value is it? So be sure that you check the fire-proof factor of any safe that you plan to buy. Also make sure your safe is large enough and heavy enough to discourage thieves from removing it from your home. You may want to make sure it is securely attached to further discourage theft.

For further protection, you should insure all your valuables against loss, theft, or damage.

The U.S Government: A Bargain Hunter's Paradise

Perhaps you have heard many times about the fantastic bargains you can get on just about any piece of merchandise by buying it wholesale from Uncle Sam.

But is it really true that the U.S. Government has all this cheap stuff for sale — or is it just a persistent myth?

The bottom line answer is this: Yes! It's true that the U.S. Government has an almost unlimited amount of items for sale at dirt-cheap, rock-bottom prices. From very large items, like houses and cars, to the tiniest, like jewelry and electronics, the government is in a constant state of selling off things it doesn't want.

The U.S. Government has a steady, endless, unstoppable supply of bargain-basement merchandise that shrewd buyers have been snapping up and reselling at enormous profits for decades. It's time you learned the ropes of the U.S. surplus merchandise market and started taking your share. The potential and opportunities to find super deals on the merchandise that you want, or to make enormous amounts of cash through resale of items you buy cheap are virtually unlimited.

But there's more. Remember that when it comes to surplus buying, knowledge is truly power. And there is no greater source of knowledge about domestic and international surplus merchandise than the U.S. Government. Furthermore, federal agencies, such as the International Trade Commission and the U.S. Department of Commerce have toll free numbers and experts on hand to answer any and all questions you might have. By just picking up a phone or by writing to the proper department, you can obtain vast amounts of information about every possible aspect of domestic and international surplus merchandise buying.

So in this section we'll first look at what products the government has for sale at bargain prices, and then we'll take a tour through the various government trade agencies and how you can access them.

From Airplanes to Zithers:
You Can Probably Buy It (wholesale) From Uncle Sam

Here's what a recent article in OMNI Magazine said about what's available from the U.S. Government:

"Has Uncle Sam got a deal for you. Government auctions offer bargain prices on a wider array of merchandise than you'll find in a Neiman Marcus Christmas catalog ... with a little luck and legwork, shrewd shoppers can get good deals on pricey or unusual items."

For example, government laboratories of all sorts often sell microscopes, centrifuges, signal generators, office furniture, computers, electronics of all sorts — and more than 40,000 automobiles per year.
Other examples: the Resolution Trust Organization. It sells houses, condos, hotels, land. The U.S. Postal Service: It sells televisions, CDs, cameras — all from unclaimed packages.

In short, the variety and amount of products available from the government is virtually endless. The only downside to it all is that experienced buyers and traders have learned to play the government merchandise gravy train like a piano, so newcomers may find stiff competition. But everyone has to start somewhere, and you can try your hand at getting in on the action and making some excellent deals.

One way to get ahead of the game is to take advantage of the inspection period before items are sold. Inspections are usually done a day or two before merchandise is sold. Here is what OMNI magazine recommends:

"Carefully examine the merchandise and then figure out what comparable items would cost if they were being sold retail. To avoid getting swept up in bidding fever — and overpaying for something you don't really want — determine exactly what you want to buy and how much you intend to spend, and stick to it."

You may have already seen or heard about ads which tout government surplus merchandise and promise "insider information." But these ads are almost always rip-offs so you should avoid them. It's better that you go straight to the source for any information that you need about government surplus merchandise. Contact the General Services Administration. They publish a free booklet, The U.S. General Services Administration Guide to Federal Government Sales. It will tell you everything you need to know. To obtain the publication write to:

Consumer Information Center
Dept. 601Z
Pueblo, CO 81009

Also, Major sales by the U.S. Marshall's Service are advertised on the Third Wednesday of every month in the classified section of USA Today. You can also call Manheim Auction toll free at 800-222-9885.

Getting "inside" Government Information:
Tapping the Resources Your Tax Dollars Pay For

Now that you know that the U.S. Government has lots and lots of stuff to sell, it's time for you to get connected to those people and agencies that will open up a tremendous amount of opportunities for you. There are dozens of government reports, manuals, books, catalogs and other information that will provide you with incredible insights to all the workings of government surplus merchandise buying and selling. Let's look at some of them and what they can offer to you:

International Competition Resources and Exports

Commerce Productivity Center
U.S. Dept. of Commerce
14th St & Constitution Ave. NW Room 7413
Washington, D.C. 20230
Telephone: 202-377-0940
This agency has more than 35 experts on hand who can help you
with everything from economic policy in foreign countries to
patent policy. They have dozens of publications which can help you
in national and international trading efforts.

Office of Service Industries
U.S. Dept of Commerce
Room 2812
Washington, D.C. 20230
Telephone: 202-377-3575
The Office of Service Industries is a very important entity for
merchandise traders. It deals with trade policy and promotion
matters that affect the foreign business sector of U.S. service
industries and helps solve their problems.

The International Trade Administration
U.S. Dept. of Commerce
14 and Constitution Ave. NW Room 442
Washington, D.C. 20230
Telephone: 202-377-4356
The ITA can refer you to an industry specialist for nearly every
industry in the United States, and answer any conceivable question
you might have on any kind of merchandise you may be interested
in trading.

Office of Instrumentation and Medical Sciences
Sciences and Electronics Cluster
International Trade Administration
U.S. Dept. of Commerce
Washington, D.C. 20230
Telephone 202-377-0550
If you are interested in the high-tech, high thrill business of buying
and selling medical equipment on the international market, this is
the agency to contact for help. They can tell you about the volumes
of shipments of domestic manufacturers, international
trade data, including exports and imports!

Roadmap

Office of Business Liaison, Room 5898C
Dept. of Commerce
Washington D.C. 20230
Telephone: 202-377-3176
Just what you need! A roadmap through the maze of our
government. This is it. It's a free information service established by
the Dept. of Commerce which is designed to help you find any
agency, or get any bit of information you need from a government
entity. The staff of Roadmap will help you deal with any
government agency or help find someone who can if they can't.
Most importantly for our purposes, Roadmap will tell you just about
anything you want to know about importing and exporting
merchandise.

Trade Statistic Division
Herbert Hoover Bldg. Room 2217
Dept. of Commerce
Washington D.C. 20230
Telephone: 202-377-4211
This entity will provide you with a quarterly publication about
international trade and trends, which may help you get an inside tip
on any number of items. The name of the publication is
"International Economic Indicators and Competitive Trends.

Office of Trade Information Service (OTIS)
Dept. of Commerce
P.O. Box 14207
Washington, D.C. 20044
Telephone: 202-377-2665 or 202-337-2432

Don't miss this vital resource! OTIS provides reports and services
on the marketing of products with an international scope.
including a contact service which puts you in contact with
distributors, manufacturers, retailers and wholesalers in the country
of your choice. When you contact OTIS, ask first for their Trade
List. It provides a list of agents, manufacturers, distributors,
retailers and wholesalers of products of worldwide scope! The
Trade List is a 126-page book and costs about $40.

Another OTIS gem is the Trade Opportunities Bulletin. This
valuable tool is a weekly publication consisting of trade leads for all
types of products.

Yet another must have OTIS publication in their Export Mailing List. It provides a custom mailing list of manufacturers of specific products for a country.

In summary...

No one who wants to get into merchandise buying and selling can afford to ignore the gigantic influence the federal government has on all aspects of trade. Not only is the U.S. government a major source of rock-bottom products which you can buy and re-sell, it is perhaps, more importantly, the ultimate source of knowledge about all aspects of surplus trade, foreign and domestic. By contacting the above sources you will soon begin to fill up an impressive library of facts and information about domestic and international surplus merchandise. You might find a lot of the information dry and statistical, but you will also find a gold mine of the very information you need to find yourself incredible bargains — or to make yourself rich by reselling items you have bought at 10 percent of the actual value!

Social Security - It isn't just for "old" people.

Social Security is a part of your life whether you like it or not. If you don't like it, we won't try to convince you to like it. We would guess that if you are young and have figured out how much you will pay into it by the time you retire, you don't much like the program. However, if you are retired and drawing a monthly check, you probably like the idea but are not too thrilled with the size of the check. Social Security does have its bad points. The tens of thousands of dollars that you will probably end up paying for it is one of them - if you earn more than the maximum Social Security taxable income, you are paying in over $5000 per year and your employer pays a matching amount for you. If you are self employed you get to pay the whole $10,000 yourself.

When you look at the amount you will be "contributing" before you can draw, it makes sense to know what benefits are available to you. It's surprising how little people actually know about this monster program that feeds off their every paycheck.

We've all heard people predict that Social Security won't even be around by the time they are ready to retire. That probably isn't true.

It does, however, make sense to work out a retirement program that doesn't depend solely on Social Security benefits.

Social Security was never intended to be a total retirement package - it was established as a supplement to your other retirement funds. Social Security benefits on the average are about at poverty levels now. You should assume that benefits will become less in proportion to cost of living as the retired population increases and the working population decreases - and the population is doing just that because of the high birth rate during baby boom and the declining birth rate since then. You might also expect that there will be new rules to disqualify independently wealthy persons.

Are you thinking, "But, hey! Don't I get back what I put in?" The answer is, "NO!" What you are paying in to the program now goes to pay the people who are getting benefits now. When you are ready to receive benefits, the people who are working at that time will be footing the bill - and that's why you might anticipate problems as the population distribution shifts.

Your benefit eligibility depends on the number of credits you have - you must have at least 40 credits. Credits are simply how many fiscal quarters you have participated in the program. Participation comes down to whether you have earned at least $50 - and paid Social Security tax on it - in a fiscal quarter. If you have worked for wages full time for ten years, no problem, you have qualified.

You probably look at Social Security as a retirement plan - although by this time we hope you are looking it as merely a small part of your retirement package. But Social Security is much more than just supplemental retirement income.

People who are a lot younger than retirement age can get benefits, too.

No matter what their age, your survivors can draw benefits - if you have worked the qualifying quarters - when you die. The qualifying quarters for survivor's benefits are less than what you need to qualify for retirement benefits - based on your last three years. If, when you die, your spouse is left to care for children who are under 16-years old or disabled, he/she is eligible for benefits. Your unmarried children under eighteen (19 if in high school) are eligible. Your dependent grandchildren - under certain circumstances - and dependent parents - if over 62 - are also eligible. If you die while you are on Social Security, your spouse would be eligible for full benefits at age 65 or partial benefits at age 60. If your spouse is disabled, his/her qualifying age could drop to 50.

At any age, you could get benefits if you become disabled. Your application for disability is checked out thoroughly to see if you meet Social Security's definition of disabled. You may not qualify for Social Security benefits even though you have qualified for disability insurance. If you are working and earning more than $500 dollars a month, you won't qualify.

Social Security has a list of disabilities that automatically qualify for benefits. If your condition is on their list, you qualify. If your condition is not on their list, they will determine if your disability is as severe as those on the list, and whether your condition interferes with the work you've been doing for the past fifteen years. If they decide you can't do the work you've been doing, they then check over your age, experience, skills, and other qualities to see if you could do some other type of work. If they decide that you can't reasonably be expected to work, you will qualify for benefits. Of course, you must also have enough credits to qualify. The number of credits required is dependent upon how old you are when you become disabled.

Some of your family members may also qualify for benefits if you become disabled: your spouse, if over 62; your spouse, if caring for your child or children who are under 16 or disabled; your unmarried children who are under 18 (19 if in high school) or disabled, your dependent grandchildren.

If you have been working steadily and making between $20,000 and $55,000 and become disabled, you can expect benefits of around $750 to over $1250 per month. If you have a spouse and children, the total family benefits could be over $1600 per month.

As we all know, Social Security is also a retirement plan. To get maximum benefits from the program, you should be aware of the way your retirement benefits are computed and how the options that are available to you work. There ARE ways you can get more money from Social Security. All it takes is knowing how the program works and doing a little planning.

The size of your retirement check is computed by averaging your earnings over most of your life. However, your most recent earnings count more. So, if possible, it is important to make heavy contributions in the last years before you retire. The higher your earnings over your lifetime, the higher your benefits will be - which means that if you have had some poor years, your benefits will probably be lower. If you take an early retirement option, it will mean that your monthly payments will be less - but not necessarily that you will receive less TOTAL benefits.

If you take the early retirement option, you do get less per month. But you will have collected longer. If you retire at age 62, for instance, you will have three years of benefits before age 65. So, although your monthly benefit is smaller, you will have already collected a sizable sum before age 65. So you will be ahead in total benefits until about age 77. But there are two things to consider here. First, your MONTHLY benefits will always be smaller. Second, increases for inflation are computed on a percentage basis so your cost of living increases will be smaller, too. The ages used here are for demonstration purposes - the ages for early and full retirement may be different for you. But it is important to look at the effect early retirement has.

If you have a separate retirement plan that provides for your needs so that you are not depending on Social Security for basic needs, early retirement is not a bad option. However, if you need the money to live on, you should carefully think over the effect early retirement will have on your monthly benefits.

What about your separate retirement plan? If you have income from interest, dividends, and pensions, will you get less benefits from Social Security? No. This kind of income - called unearned income - does not affect the amount of your benefits. However, if it is a sizable amount, it can put you over the income tax limit. That means you might end up having to pay taxes on a portion of your Social Security benefits. If all of your taxable income - from wages, interest, dividends, taxable pensions, etc. - plus one half of your Social Security benefits is less than $25,000 for singles or more than $32,000 for married couples, you probably don't owe any taxes. And if you do owe taxes, you will only be taxed on a portion of your income - half of your Social Security benefits or half of the amount your exceed the income limit, whichever is larger.

Earned income - from working at a job - can actually reduce your benefit check, though. The amount you can earn before benefits are reduced depends on your age. The age guidelines and ratio of reduction are in the process of being adjusted.

Other people may be able to receive benefits from your contributions, too.

If your spouse is not eligible for benefits on his/her own work record, he/she can draw an amount equal to one half of your benefits. What if your spouse is eligible for benefits based on his/her own work record, but it is less than the one half benefit based on your work record? He/she will get the larger of the two!

If you have dependent children under the age of 18 (19 if in high school) at the time that you retire, they are eligible for benefits. Your children who were disabled before they were age 22, are eligible for benefits when you retire. Dependent grandchildren at the time of your retirement may be eligible for benefits.

Your former spouse may be eligible for benefits based on your work record! If your former spouse is age 62 or older, if you were married ten or more years, if you have been divorced at least two years, if he/she did not remarry before age 60 - he/she may be entitled to benefits based on your work record. But don't worry - the amount the ex gets won't affect the amounts you and your current spouse and family can get.

No one gets benefits without applying. Social Security benefits do not automatically begin when you are disabled or of retirement age. You must apply. Being aware of what you can apply for and how your options will affect your benefits is important.

You should apply for Social Security benefits at least three months before you intend to retire - they have a lot of applications to process. Apply for medicare within three months of your sixty-fifth birthday.

It's very important to know if your contributions are being applied to your account properly. Mistakes can happen! You have the right to check on your account. You can call 1-800-772-1213. Ask them to send you a form. Complete it and return it and they will mail you a history of your earnings and an estimate of your retirement benefits.

You should check these statements every few years to make sure that you are getting credit for your earnings.

Whether you like it or not, Social Security is a part of your life and you will pay a lot of money into the program during your working life. It only makes sense to know what you can get in return and plan carefully so you get the maximum benefits that you have paid for.

Torts

Each of us protected from invasion of our private and personal rights by federal and state laws and constitutions. Everyone - including private citizens and companies and corporations - is charged with the duty of observing and respecting these rights. Any breach of this is a tort. In other words, a tort is a wrongful act that injures you or damages your property. This does not include breach of contract, although a breach of contract can occur at the same time as a tort. Personal injury torts can also include psychological trauma.

The law attempts to provide relief for you in the event of a tort. The person or company who commits the tort is responsible for the damages to you that occur from that act even if the damages were not intentional.

Tort law leans to favoring you as the injured party.

A suit involving a tort differs from a criminal suit. In a criminal suit the accused must be proved guilty "beyond a reasonable doubt." In a tort, the accused need only be proved to be responsible for the tort and the resulting damages "by a fair preponderance of credible evidence." As you can see, proving responsibility for a tort can be a far easier task than proving guilt in a criminal case.

In addition, you as the injured party will have no trouble finding a lawyer to represent you on a contingency fee basis - for a percentage of what you are awarded. The accused will have to pay cash for every hour their lawyer works on the case.

There is a rule that other awards you may have received for the injury cannot be brought up in court. In other words, it is possible to win a large award for an injury although you may have been covered by your insurance and already been awarded medical and disability funds through them.

In the case of negligence - the easiest tort to bring to court - the court must decide if you had a duty to act in a given manner. Then it must be decided if you failed to act in that manner. They must also decide if the accused had a duty to act in a given manner and failed to do so. In other words, they are deciding who acted negligently. If both you and the accused behaved in a negligent manner, you may still be awarded damages if they feel the accused was more negligent than you were. The intention of the accused is does not matter - only that he failed to use the required care and diligence in the situation.

Defamation, slander, and libel are all violations of the right to enjoy a good reputation. To be actionable a defamation must be published or communicated, AND as the injured party, you must prove willful and malicious intent. Damages do not have to be proved. Proving malicious intent can be quite difficult - especially for public figures, who are must accept a different situation called "fair comment" which limits them more than the private citizen in bringing suit for defamation. Also comments made during a trial or in the political arena are rarely prosecutable.

When your right to hold and use your real property is interfered with and damage results it is a tort. This is actionable and you have a right to recovery.

If you are injured on private property due to the negligence of the owner in caring for the property and keeping it free from hazards, then the owner is financially responsible for the consequences of your injury. The degree of responsibility may depend upon the reason you came on the property unless the injury occurred as a result of gross negligence.

Malpractice - errors and omissions a professional commits in discharging his/her duty - are also torts. If you are injured because a professional that you have retained did not discharge his/her duties properly, you are entitled to recovery.

Product liability - companies are charged with the safety of their customers in using their products. If you are injured because of an unsafe product you are entitled to recovery.

If you have suffered damages and injuries to your personal liberty, personal safety, reputation, or someone has violated your property rights, you may be entitled to recovery. Bringing a tort to suit is not a very difficult act.

Most lawyers are willing to work for you on a contingency basis - you pay little or nothing up front and they will take a percentage of what you are awarded. This way you will not be responsible to pay out a large amount if you should loose the case.

The accused, on the other hand, will have to pay cash to defend himself. Since the accused will be paying large fees per hour, it is in his/her best interests to settle with you as quickly as possible. Often it is cheaper for the accused to settle than it is to go to court even he/she expects to win! The legal fees may cost more than the settlement!

It may be to your advantage to settle out of court rather than go through the legal hassles of courtroom procedure. You may feel that you don't need the hassles on top of the injuries and damages you've already incurred.

Federal Tax Audit-

Words that can strike fear into the hearts of the bravest, most stable and level-headed adults. A federal tax audit is a fearful thing to most of us - and with reason. Instinctively, we know an audit will take time, create frustration, and cost us money. It will make even the most intelligent and honest of us feel inadequate, dumber than a doorknob, and criminal, as well.

Why? Because we know we don't really understand all the rules and regulations of filing our income tax. We know that common sense and intelligence are no guarantee of doing the darn things to the satisfaction of the IRS department. And, we've heard all the horror stories about others' audit experiences.

So, is it as bad as all that? Well, it CAN be bad, but there are things you can do to make the audit a less painful experience. It will, no doubt, still be a fearful and unpleasant thing, but not so bad as you think.

Once you have been notified of the impending audit (no, we didn't say impending doom), you will have to make an effort to keep a sense of humor about it. Because even if takes some effort, you may as well look at it with a sense of humor. Maintaining a sense of humor will help keep you sane through the ordeal - - - well, process.

OK. You have received your audit notice and we will assume you aren't laughing. What should you do?

First, you will want to decide if this is something you want to face on your own. We advise that you let your accountant or tax preparer in on the audit. In fact, it is best if you let him take care of all the direct communication with the auditor. He is in a better position to be objective about the whole thing (he isn't numb with fear). And it is important to be objective and unemotional with the auditor. Your tax preparer knows what the auditor wants to hear and will be able to discuss any problems and answer the questions more intelligently than you could (he isn't speechless with terror). If your tax preparer wants to make time to consider the tax implications of certain information, he can stall for time with a simple, "I'll have to check that with my client." Besides he is more likely to understand the jargon and what the auditor wants.

You will have to gather up all your receipts and other documents and make sure they are in order. Be sure they are orderly and understandable. Your tax preparer will likely have to find things for the auditor. It is also a good idea to go through the records and recalculate. Check the mathematics. Check transfers of figures from one record to another. Check your deductions, in particular. If you find you made a gross error when you reported, let your tax preparer know. He will take care of letting the auditor know.

But give him only your receipts for each item that is being checked - with totals. Don't volunteer anything that hasn't been requested! You do not have to give him cancelled checks, expense logs, or other backup material. If the auditor decides he needs those, he can get them at a later visit.

If you decide you want to handle this thing on your own, the same thing goes for what you say. Give him only the minimum - answer with just a yes or no. Don't say anything you don't have to. Don't volunteer anything or defend your answers unless directly questioned about your reasoning. But if you go alone, you had better be prepared to defend your every entry on your return. If you have accurate and complete records, the audit will be easier - it will be much easier to defend your entries. Your tax preparer will want those records to be accurate and complete, too, if you have wisely chosen to have him represent you at the audit.

A great deal depends upon what shape your records are in. An audit often takes place long after you filed - it can be years after - so if your records aren't clear it will be pretty difficult to defend your entries.

An audit can consist of one short visit or several visits over an extended length of time. It depends upon the thoroughness of the auditor you have been blessed with and the complexity of the return you filed. The auditor will probably operate in a less specific manner than you would like - you'll probably have to suffer a time of suspense, because the auditor does not have to give you any specific results right away. But you will be notified of those, too, sooner or later.

And what will be the result? That will depend on how accurately your return was completed, how well you handled the audit interviews, and your auditor's opinions about what are allowable deductions (and, of course, whether he and his wife are getting along). And that is why we become so frustrated - some of these matters we have absolutely no control over.

But whatever the result, be prepared to pay. It will, no doubt, cost you money. Sometimes they decide that you did a good job of deciding what to put on the form, so you don't owe them any money. Sometimes they will disallow a deduction or change a depreciation schedule or something so you do owe them some money. Whatever the auditor decides, you will more than likely end up owing your tax preparer for his services. But cheer up! You probably won't end up in jail - unless, of course, you have been deliberately defrauding the government. But even then, a check can usually buy forgiveness.

So an audit isn't the end of the world. But it is tense and frustrating and most of us would like to avoid it.

What are your chances of being audited and how can you reduce them?

Well, every year more than two million "invitations" are sent out to reluctant guest (not many of these invitations are declined, by the way). Most of the time, you are chosen for an audit by a computer program. The computer scans returns looking for items that may indicate an error. Large deductions in comparison to your income is one. Some are randomly selected by the computer that have no questionable items.

Some types of deductions that auditors examine closely are those that you are not likely to have adequate documentation for. If you have had losses due to vandalism, accidents, floods, fires, storms, and the like, you may be picked for an audit.

Since child care is often paid in cash. If you have a large claim for child-care expenses, be sure to document it carefully. Get receipts.

Charitable contributions are carefully checked. For your protection, always ask for receipts to back your claims.

Also, handle auto and entertainment deductions carefully.

If your return has been examined in one of the two previous years for the same items they are questioning this year and that audit resulted in no extra payment, you can call the IRS. The audit will likely be suspended.

Once the computer kicks out your return for audit, will you automatically be audited? No. Your return is reviewed by IRS employees, and they make the final decision on whether or not to audit your return.

You can stop the process right there. In fact, many returns that have been kicked out are never audited. Some people never even know that their return was chosen by the IRS computer for an audit!

So, what can you do to stop the IRS from auditing you? Prepare your return correctly. If it is apparent that there is no error on it, the IRS employee who reviews it will overturn the computer's decision and you will not be audited. If you have unusual or unusually large deductions, include proof of the deductions with your return-receipts from charities, receipts for other deductions - so that the reviewing agent will know that you have not made an error and to convince him that there is no need for examining any further. (When you include receipts or proof with your return, always be sure to keep a copy for your records.) He will overturn the audit - and you will probably never know that the IRS computer picked your number!

Making a will

Have you made a will? It is one of the most neglected and postponed aspects of personal finance plans. It's easy to shrug it off.

Excuses abound: You don't want to think about it. You're too young to worry about it. You don't have enough assets to need a will. Everything will take care of itself anyway.

BUT, you are never too young to think about security for your family and loved ones - we all know that there are no guarantees of a lengthy life. Anyway, it's easier to do it when you are young and death seems like a remote possibility. And a will is important whether you are rich or poor, male or female. Preparing the document will make you look at your provisions for your family - help you make decisions and plans now that can be more effectively implemented because you are young. Of course, if you are not young, it is extremely important to take care of a will now.

If you think you haven't enough assets to worry about it, you will likely be surprised when you begin preparing your will. Most of us underestimate the value of our assets. You will also become aware of your interest in controlling a few things after your death - like who will administer your property and how it should be administered and who will be guardian of your children. You also will find that you can make things easier for your loved ones in the event of your death. It will be a difficult enough time for them - they should not have to deal with the delays and complications and inconveniences that dying without a will may create.

Of course, if you die intestate (without a will), it is true that "things will take care of themselves." Eventually, your estate will be settled, even if it is not the way you or your loved ones would like to see it done.

When you die intestate, the state has made a "will" for you - they will settle your estate. They will decide who gets your property, who will be the guardian of your children, and all other concerns of your estate. Their decisions probably would not be the decisions you would make, and the costs for this unsatisfactory settlement can be enormous.

You should not make a quickie will. This is a step that requires a lot of thought and planning. You'll want to decide how your estate should be taken care of and who will get certain of your possessions. Plan carefully.

If you have a "live-in" partner who you want to leave property to it is essential that you have a will. Unmarried couples DO NOT have the same rights as married couples under the inheritance laws, so plan EXTRA carefully if you have a live-in. Your partner could end up losing out even if your intention is to provide for him/her. You must be very careful when making provisions for your partner in your will. Be very specific about who gets what and why.

In planning what you want to do with your estate, you should be aware of the different types of legal options that are available - and examine them in relation to your situation. If you consult a lawyer, don't just blindly accept what he has to say - YOU are the expert on your financial and family situation. YOU must decide what is the best route to take.

The only way to really know what is the best route is to learn which legal will or trust is best for you.

There are many varieties of trusts. These are often used not only to transfer property but to reduce taxes. There are many real concerns in establishing a trust. For instance, if your main objective is to reduce income and estate taxes, you should appoint an unrelated, independent person or institution as trustee - your trustee is the person who controls the trust. Having someone who is unrelated holding the position of trustee is uncomfortable for some people. Although you can get by with appointing a relative and an independent party as co-trustees, the relative can be outvoted. Other concerns are the fees (administration of the trust is not free) and the experience and qualifications of the trust department you have chosen.

You can make either a revocable or an irrevocable trust. Although there are many varieties of trusts, each is either revocable or irrevocable. This simply means that either you retain the right to change the trust or you surrender that right.

A revocable trust will eliminate the delays and inconvenience of probate - your assets under the trust do not have to be put through probate. This type of trust is not subject to public inspection. There is no tax advantage with a revocable trust.

An irrevocable trust will provide tax advantages. When the property you put in the trust appreciates in value, the appreciation will not be subject to gift or estate taxes. However, you have little control over this trust and YOU CAN NOT CHANGE IT.

.A living trust is one that you put all your assets into while you are still living. Many lawyers recommend this type of trust because, if it is irrevocable, upon your death nothing will be probated - you no longer own anything individually. Also, the management of your estate will not be affected by your death. If you make a revocable living trust, you lose the tax benefits - and it does become irrevocable upon your death. An irrevocable living trust is NOT a good idea. As we said, an irrevocable trust cannot be altered or changed. In effect, you will have surrendered much of your control over your assets. You should retain control over your assets while you are still living.

Other varieties of trusts are available but - if you have relatively limited assets, you have never made a will before, and you're mainly interested in orderly transfer of property - trusts are probably not the way for you to go. Trusts can be a waste of time and money. Your first step should probably be a will.

There are advantages to making a will rather than a trust.

You can change a will whenever you want - in fact, you should whenever you have a family change. A marriage, a divorce, new babies, disablement or death of a loved one are all reasons for a will change. In fact, depending on the state you live in, these things may make your will invalid.

Your will is private - no one need see it. You should have witnesses to the signing of it, but they don't need to see what is in it. They merely have to verify that the signature is yours. The will does become a public document upon your death, though.

Where do you begin? Well, as we said, you must do some careful planning.

Decide who you want to appoint as guardians for your children. This should be discussed with the prospective guardians, by the way. If you choose to do so, you can designate guardians for the care of your children and separate guardians to administer the children's financial affairs. If you have a living spouse, it is important for each of you to have a will specifying guardianships for minor children in the event that both of you die. You will need the full names and addresses of the guardians you have chosen.

Decide how you want your property divided. If you have children, you need not leave equal amounts to each. For instance, if some have special needs, you make your decisions accordingly.

If you have limited assets, it is probably best to leave your entire assets to your spouse. Leaving portions of your assets to minor children could tie them up creating hardship for your family.

You cannot legally disinherit a spouse. He/she is entitled to a minimum by law. If your will attempts to disinherit him/her, it will be over-ridden and your entire will may be declared invalid.

Be sure when you are planning the disposal of your assets that you hold out enough liquid assets to pay "death expenses" so that your real property will not have to be sold to get money to pay them. These expenses will include funeral expenses, income and estate taxes, probate taxes, real estate taxes, administration fees, probate fees, and others. So don't designate beneficiaries for all of the liquid assets.

You will need the full names and addresses of all of your beneficiaries.

You will need to choose an executor of your estate. An executor is a person who will make sure your wishes are carried out according to your instructions in the will. This person will be responsible for paying the "death expenses" and liquidating property to pay them if necessary. You can appoint your spouse or another relative - the advantage is that they are familiar with your property and with your wishes. However, the executor has a lot complicated financial responsibilities, especially if your estate is quite large. You can appoint a relative and a professional financial person as co-executors if you wish. This would have the advantage of both family knowledge and financial expertise.

In looking over your affairs and planning how you want your affairs taken care of after your death, you have probably thought about illness, anatomical gifts, and funerals. You probably have come to some conclusions that you would like to include in your will. These things should be addressed in separate documents.

If you do not wish to be kept on life support systems when there is no hope of recovery and want to make those wishes known, a separate document known as a living will (obviously totally different from a living trust!) should be drawn up. Do not include this information in your regular will. The laws governing living wills vary depending on the state you live in. Your best bet is to contact:

Choice in Dying
200 Varick Street
New York, NY 10014
Telephone (212) 366-5540

If you wish to make anatomical gifts (organ donations), use a special state-approved form and carry a donor card. This information is relatively useless in a will. For one thing, your will may not be reviewed until several days after your death.

If you have specific instructions about the type of funeral you want or how you want your remains disposed of you can put them in your regular will, but again the time factor for reviewing the will may be a problem. It would be better to put this information in a letter that you keep separate from your will. Be sure someone is aware of the letter and its location.

OK. You have done a lot of planning about how you want your affairs taken care of. Now what does a will contain?

First, you need a statement that includes your full name and current address and the date. This statement should declare that this is a will and that you are revoking any previous wills made by you. This should be included even if you have never drawn up a formal will before.

You may want to include specific bequests concerning cash, stocks, and bonds. Be sure you have decided if you want to transfer appreciating stocks, etc. at the current value or at future value. State this clearly.

You also may want to include specific bequest concerning personal property. Personal property is any property that is not real estate and includes your automobiles, jewelry, recreational vehicles, books, collections, etc. When you bequest personal property it is important to describe the property clearly so there will be no misunderstanding. For instance, "my diamond-onyx ring to my son, John."

A general bequest does not name an item specifically. For instance, "all my tools in my garage to my son, John." If you want to specify multiple beneficiaries in a general bequest, you should specify how it is to be divided. For instance, "all my tools in my garage to my sons, John and Tom, in equal shares. Be sure to use my or other qualifiers when describing your property to avoid any legal hassles in the event that you are no longer in possession of that property at the time of your death.

You may want to include directions for the disposal of your real property. You will have to know what type of title you have on each piece of property. Under some joint titles the property is automatically transferred. These should not be included in your will. Deal very carefully with real property.

You will want to include instructions for the residuary. Residuary is merely the amount of your estate that is left over after the other instructions are taken care of. You may want to include a statement that all taxes be paid from the residuary. You can make other arrangements for the taxes, however.

You should include a simultaneous death clause. This states who will receive your property in the event that you and your beneficiary die at the same time. You need to include the names of the guardians you have chosen for your children. You need to include the names of your chosen executor or executors.

You MUST sign the document and have the signature witnessed. In your state witnesses may not be required, but we recommend that you have your signature witnessed anyway. That way the signature can't be questioned.

You should have only ONE original of your will, but you should have copies, unsigned, as well. Keep the original in a safe place. We do NOT recommend a safe deposit box for a will because there may be delays in obtaining it. In some states a court procedure is required to open a safe deposit box after you die.

This all may seem very complicated, but in most cases it really isn't that difficult. Most likely you will want to leave nearly everything to your spouse, so it will be pretty easy to do your will. All it takes is a little planning and care in drawing up the document. There are forms available to make the chore easier. A simple will is perfectly good and effective unless your estate is large or the disposal instructions unusually complicated.

A simple will is easy and the cost is minimal, so why wait? Everyone should have a will. Forms can be purchased at your local stationery store. Do it!

CONCLUSION

We hope that you found in this book what you have been seeking. We've done the best we could to show you hundreds of ways that you can succeed, to stimulate your mind, and to bring you new and innovative ideas. Now, the rest is up to you. Keep this in mind: Even the best weight loss book in the world will not cause a person to lose weight simply by the fact that he or she has read the book. The best financial plan in the world will not make you rich unless you implement that plan in an intelligent way in your life. The latest methods of meeting new people will do you no good if you cower in the privacy of your own home, afraid to put the method to use. In order for the ideas presented within any book, plan or strategy to work, the person who has learned those ideas must put them into practice! Whether it is a weight loss book, a get rich quick plan, or a scheme to improve your life -- they're all just ideas until YOU make them a reality. Ideas within themselves are not real "things". In fact, most experienced, successful people will tell you that coming up with an idea is the easiest part of any venture. It's taking those ideas out of the realm of mind and into the solid world of reality that takes, sweat, persistence and plain old hard work. The plans and ideas in this book are waiting for you to breathe life into them. They are waiting for you to integrate them within your world so that you can have the things you want and the life you have always dreamed of. Now that you have the tools, there's nothing to stop you. This book has given you the tools you need for a happy, successful fulfilling life. Why not go out and make that life your own? Why not start right now? Start today! Wishing you all success and prosperity -- good luck!

YOU MAY CUT ALONG THE DOTTED LINE AND KEEP THESE REPORTS IN A SEPARATE FOLDER FOR FUTURE REFERENCE.

FREE REPORTS

Airline safety

Airline fatalities are infrequent. In fact, your chances of being injured or killed in an airline mishap are very small indeed -- far less than your chances of being injured in your automobile. Never-the-less, it makes sense to reduce the risks further with some simple precautions.

Put off your flight

If the weather predicted is bad at either end of the flight, put off going if you can, and hold a refundable ticket.

Dress for safety

Flat, non-skid shoes will facilitate a quicker escape and won't puncture evacuation slides. Clothing of natural fibers covering most of your body will protect against fires. Synthetic fibers burn more quickly. Carry a wet washcloth in a plastic bag to breath through in case of smoke or fumes.

Safety belt

Keep your safety belt snug and buckled. An unbuckled belt is dangerous in case of unexpected turbulence.

Children's safety

Although very young children fly free if they sit on your lap, they are safer buckled into an FAA-approved booster in the seat next to you.

Where you sit

You have probably heard that the seats to the back of the plane are the safest. Statistics don't bear this out. It depends on how the plane crashes. Choose a seat with an easy escape route. Before take-off, check out the escape route. Count the seats to the escape doors. In the event of a crash, the cabin make be dark or full of smoke. If you know the number of seats to the emergency exit, you can "feel" your way out.

Protect your home from burglary

Burglaries are more of a threat today than ever before. Also, they can occur at any time -- day or night and even when someone is home.

Lock up

Just locking up the place will help. According to the Department of Justice National Crime Victimization Survey, about half of completed burglaries occur in homes where doors or windows are simply unlocked.

Choosing locks for your doors

The right locks for your doors are important. If your lock can be picked, slipped, or kicked open in less than five minutes, many burglars won't be deterred. The typical entrance lockset has a secondary latch that can't be slipped with a credit card but the latches are short. Consider installing a double cylinder deep throw deadbolt lock (keyed cylinder on both exterior and interior), as well. This gives you deadbolt security both when you're absent and when you're home.

Install locks properly

When installing your locksets, don't use the short screws that come with most strike plates. Get three-inch screws that will penetrate into the framing studs.

Before installing new locks

Check out your doors and jambs. If the door itself isn't solid and secure, a secure lock is pointless. Make sure your door fits snugly so a hacksaw blade can't be inserted to cut the latch or bolt.

Remove temptation

Don't leave tempting items where they can be easily seen. Position computers, TVs, VCRs, stereos away from windows.

Driveway and garage caution

Driveways are becoming high risk areas. Always keep your garage locked. Make sure no one ducks in while you pull in or out. When you come home, scan your driveway before you get out of your car.

While you're away

Set up timers to turn lights off and on. Stop newspaper and mail delivery. Have the lawn mowed or the walk shoveled. Ask neighbors to keep an eye on your place.

Little tricks

Do you spend hours attempting to remove the price tag glue on newly purchased items? End the frustration and do the job in minutes with a tissue soaked in rubbing alcohol!

Have you melted a bread bag against your hot toaster and found it impossible to remove? Rub petroleum jelly (vaseline) on the spot, heat up the toaster, and rub it off with a paper towel. For an effectively disinfecting dishes, add a squirt of bleach to your dishwater every time you do dishes. Your dishes will get sparkling clean, as well.

Can't get those rust spots out of clothes? Wet the article and rub on cream of tartar. Then place it in the sun. Or try lemon juice and place in the sun. For a sparkling streak-free shine, use old newspapers to dry your windows after washing them.

Formulas for household cleaners

You can make your own household cleaners for a fraction of what you pay for commercial cleaning products.

Window cleaners

For a window washing solution combine:
    1 cup of vinegar
    1/2 cup of ammonia
    2 tablespoons of corn starch
    3 gallons of water
    Mix well.

For a window cleaner for spray bottle use:
    2 tablespoons of Prell shampoo
    1 pint rubbing alcohol
    1 gallon water
Mix well.

Brass cleaner

A paste for cleaning brass can be made by mixing 1 tablespoon of salt with 1/2 cup vinegar and adding enough flour to make a smooth paste. Apply to item, rubbing well. Rinse with cold water.

Paint Remover

This formula uses lye. Always handle lye with care. Use enamel, porcelain, or glass containers for any lye mixture.

In a suitable container, mix together very slowly:
    1 can lye
    1 quart water

In another suitable container, combine:

2 quarts water
4 heaping tablespoons corn starch

Slowly add lye mixture to cornstarch mixture and stir carefully. The mixture will thicken. Apply with a paint brush and let stand 5 minutes. Spray with a water hose to remove. Do not let lye mixture come in contact with your skin.

Laundry soap
This formula uses lye. Always handle lye with care. Use enamel, porcelain, or glass containers for any lye mixture.

5 pounds of fat
1 can lye
6 quarts soft water
1/2 cup ammonia
1/2 cup borax

Mix in large suitable enamel ware kettle. Let stand for 5 days, stirring several times a day. (After the fourth day, it will be quite thick.)
On the sixth day, place on stove and heat slowly, stirring well several times until it becomes the consistency of honey. Let cool before pouring into mould.
For a mould, you will need a box about 1 1/2 inches deep lined first with aluminum foil and then with a towel wrung out in cold water. As soon as it is firm enough, cut into bars. Then let stand until cold. To use, cut into small pieces and add to washer in place of powdered detergent.

Stain remover for china
For china stained with tea or coffee:
-Mix 2 tablespoons of salt with enough vinegar to form a paste. Rub stain with paste.
For china stained with iron rust spots:
-Mix 2 tablespoons of salt with enough lemon juice to form a paste. Rub stain with paste.

Getting the most from your visit to the doctor
Your doctor is capable of gaining a great deal of information about your health just from peering into your orifices or looking at your fingernails or pressing areas of your body.
Never-the-less, a physician is not a magician or a mind reader. All

diagnoses are simply the result of applied knowledge. Your doctor has had many years of instruction, knows the symptoms of a tremendous number of diseases, and has access to the latest research results.

Yet, with all this impressive knowledge, every doctor ultimately depends upon you, the patient, for a proper diagnosis and method of treatment!

To get the most from a visit to any doctor, you must be prepared to tell him/her what the problem is. A vague "I don't feel good" doesn't give the doctor much chance to fix you up. There are a million diseases out there. How is he/she to narrow it down to one?

Be prepared to explain:

EXACTLY how you feel. Be able to describe your pain or other symptoms in an understandable manner. If you have other unusual symptoms that you feel are not related to the problem at hand, mention them anyway. Let the doctor decide whether they are related.

Ask yourself questions to help form a description of your symptoms. Pain, for example: Is it a sharp pain or an ache? Is it stationary pain or does it seem to move? Does it come and go or is it steady? What movements or other factors increase or decrease it?

Be prepared to answer:

When did the current problem begin? Has this happened before? How often? When? Who did you consult previously? What was the diagnosis at that time? What was done about it? Is there anything different about this episode?

Don't offer the doctor a diagnosis:

Describe all of your symptoms exactly, but don't offer a diagnosis. That's what you're paying the doctor for.

Your questions:

No doubt you have questions about your problem you would like answered. Before visiting the doctor or between visits, decide what exactly what it is you want to know. Write the questions down so you remember to ask.

Your medical history:

Have an abbreviated list of your previous illnesses handy in case the doctor wishes to see it. This doesn't have to be elaborate - just things like major illnesses and surgeries and approximate dates.

Remember you are not consulting a magician. The symptoms of many medical problems can be almost exactly the same. A proper diagnosis can only be accomplished with you and your doctor working together. He/she needs all the help you can give so a correct diagnosis and treatment can be made for you.

Doctors will appreciate you if you are prepared and can give exact and explicit answers to their questions. They do not have the time to dredge the answers to obvious questions from you.

If you are prepared, your visit can be accomplished efficiently saving both aggravation and time for you and for the physician. Don't worry if you are caught unprepared for some of the questions. That's to be expected. Just give thoughtful answers to those.

Weight loss

Weight loss is no mystery, it's mathematical. When the body burns up more calories than it takes in, it uses calories stored in the tissue.

Lose a pound

To lose one pound a week, you need to cut 500 calories a day or increase activity by 500 calories.

Moderate exercise helps take off weight by speeding up your metabolic rate so calories are burned more quickly and efficiently.

Go slowly

Rapid weight loss is not advised. A rapid weight loss achieved from a very low-calorie and very low-carbohydrate diet comes from lean tissue and water because the body will burn proteins instead of breaking down fat.

A low-fat, high-carbohydrate diet, on the other hand, raises the ratio of lean body weight to fat. Exercise improves the ratio even further.

Ratio of fat to lean and metabolization

With a higher ratio of fat to lean body weight, you will metabolize your food differently. If you are a flabby 220 pound executive, you don't need as many calories as a muscular 220 pound athlete.

Easy and convenient weight loss

What if you want to lose weight but don't have the time or inclination to count calories and fuss with special foods? A casual weight loss program can work - you simply need to burn more calories than you consume.

To lose a couple of pounds per week, you need only increase your exercise moderately and cut a couple hundred calories from your diet.

Casual exercise

Increase your exercise easily by parking a little distance from your destination and walking. Take the stairs instead of the elevator. Take a quick walk around the block in the evening.

Casual Diet

Cutting a couple of hundred calories is as simple as toting up the average number of calories you consume for dinner and reducing your portions accordingly. You don't need to give up any foods you like and you don't have to count calories every day.

For example, if your average dinner is about 800 calories, eat the same things - but eat three quarters of your usual amount. Your caloric intake will be reduced by a couple of hundred calories.

Casual magic

With this casual increase in exercise and casual cutting of dinner portions, you'll lose a couple of pounds a week with no formal exercise program, no calorie counting, no fussing with special foods, no eliminating of favorite foods!

Chromium picolinate

Chromium is an essential element of nutrition. Among other things it facilitates fat metabolism - helps you burn more calories and build muscle.

Flatten your tummy

Everyone wants a flat stomach. The good new is that when you lose weight the stomach is one of the easiest places to lose it from (especially when you include a little walking in your program)!

Of course, it does help to tighten up those muscles a bit - but you can do it without those tiresome sit-ups.

The Swim

Here's a much easier and more pleasant exercise called the swim: -Lie on your stomach with arms and legs extended and spread about 24 inches. -Raise your head and upper chest so that you can look straight ahead. Reach out and up with right arm and left leg. Hold to the count of 5. Then lower your limbs and repeat on the other side. Do 10 on each side. Now raise both arms and both legs and paddle a right-arm/left-leg combination then left-arm/right-leg combination rapidly. Do 10 paddles on each side.

Anytime exercise for busy people

If you just can't get down on the floor to exercise, try this:

This can be done at your desk, on the bus, just about anywhere - but don't do it while driving because it can make you light-headed.

Simply sit up straight and draw in your abdomen, hold to the count of 5, and release. Repeat a half dozen times. Do this several times during the day.

Easy plan to a 50 pound loss and a flat tummy

Following this easy plan, you can lose up to 50 pounds and have a flat tummy in about a year. There are quicker plans, but they aren't as easy to stick with. An added benefit is that a gradual weight loss is easier to maintain!

Quick tummy flattener

Poor posture can make you stomach look larger than it is. Straighten up and walk tall. Magically your stomach will look flatter!

Free Stuff

You can get an amazing number of free things just for asking - if you know who to write to. Below are the addresses for over one hundred items you can get absolutely free. All you have to do is write and ask for them!

Keep in mind: Postal regulations require that you put your return address on the envelope. It may take up to eight weeks before you get the item. The companies reserve the right to change or withdraw the offer. Use postcards whenever possible. State what item it is that you're requesting.

Sample request: "Please send me your free Road Atlas and Travel Guide. Thank you."

Christmas Carols
(Words and music)
John Hancock Mutual Life Insurance
Box 111
Boston, MA 02117

Silver Value Chart for U.S. and Canadian Coins
Numismatic Newsx
Iola, WI 54945

The Story of Oil Poster
Corporate Communications
Union Oil of California
PO Box 7600
Los Angeles, CA 90051

Story of Geothermal Energy
Poster
Corporate Communications
Union Oil of California
PO Box 7600
Los Angeles, CA 90051

Poster Art
International Images
215 Lexington Ave
NY, NY 10018

First Aid Facts Chart
Johnson & Johnson
Consumer Dept.
New Brunswick, NJ 08903

Back From the Dead
(Wildlife Poster)
World Wildlife Fund
1601 Connecticut Ave, NW
Washington, DC 20009

Poison & Overdose Chart
Mead Johnson
Evansville, IN 4772

Freedom From Hunger Poster
The Food & Agriculture
Organization of the United
Nations
1325 "C" Street SW
Washington, DC 20437

Basic Nutrition Chart
Del Monte Kitchens
Box 8032
Clinton, IA 52732

Quarter Horse Poster
American Quarter Horse Assn
Amarillo, TX 79168

Road Atlas and Travel Guide
Best Western
Box 10203
Phoenix, AZ 85064

Your Social Security
Social Security Administration
Public Information Division
Baltimore, MD 21235

Favorite Rice Recipes
Rice Council
Box 22802
Houston, TX 77027

Cycling Safety Rules Chart
Employers insurance of Wausau
Safety & Health Services Dept
Wausau, WI 54401

Mail Order Magazine
(Request sample issue)
Mail Order Information Station
Box 762, Terminal Annex
Lewiston, ID 83501

Sparetime Money Making
Opportunities
(Request sample issue)
The Kipen Publishing Co.
5810 W Oklahoma Ave
Milwaukee, WI 53219

Moneymaking Opportunities
 (Request sample issue)
Success Publishing Co.
13263 Ventura Blvd.
Studio City, CA 91604

The American Buffalo
National Buffalo Assn
BOX 706
Custer, SD 57730

Fire Prevention Chart Liberty
Mutual Insurance
Public Relations Dept
175 Berkeley St
Boston, MA 02117

Blistex Lip Ointment (Sample)
(Send self-addressed stamped
envelope)
Blistex Sample Offer
1800 Swift Drive
Oak Brook, IL 60521

Free Samples and Sales Kit
American Unifax, Inc.
95 Madison Ave
New York, NY 10016

A Guide to Renting an Apartment
Public Relations Department
State Farm Insurance Company
Bloomington, IL 61701

House Hunter's Guide
Chicago Title
Booklet T2
Chicago, IL 60602

Wedding Invitation Samples
Rexcraft
Rexburg, ID 83441

Wedding & Stationery Samples
Dawn Stationery
300 Main St
Lumberton, NJ 08048

Mickey Mouse and Goofy Explore
Energy (Comic Book)
Public Affairs Dept.
Exxon USA
PO Box 2180
Houston, TX 77001

Chicken Recipes (Include self-
addressed stamped envelope)
Delmarva Poultry Industry
Box 47
Georgetown, DE 19947

Journal of Our Dog
(Dog training booklet)
Dog Care Division
Ralston Purina
Checkerboard Square
St Louis, MO 63199

How to Hold a Garage Sale
United Van Lines
1 United Dr
Fenton, MO 63026

Cholesterol, Fat, & Your Health
(Put the word FREE on outside of
envelope)
Consumer Information
Pueblo, CO 81009

Books For Kids About Moving
The Beckins Company
910 Grand Central Ave
Glendale, CA 91201

A Woman's Guide to Social Security
SS Administration
Public information
Baltimore, MD 21235

Dough It Yourself
Christmas Decorations
Salt Sculpture Booklet
Morton Salt
PO Box 373
Kankakee, IL 60902

How to Save a Choking Victim
Aetna
151 Farmington Ave
Hartford, CT 06156

Geothermal Energy Coloring Book
Corporate Communications
Union Oil of California
PO Box 7600
Los Angeles, CA 90051

Sidney Coloring Book
Sidney Coloring Book
Wool Bureau
200 Clayton Street
Denver, CO 80206

How Shall I Tell My Daughter?
Person Products
Box 1001
Milltown, NJ 08850

Hagerty's Silver Polish (Sample)
W.J. Hagerty, Ltd.
Box 1496
3801 W Linden Ave
South Bend, Indiana 46624

Car Buying and Selling Book
Shell Answer Books
Box 61609
Houston, TX 77208

The Secret Service Story
U.S. Secret Service, Rm 941
1800 G St, NW
Washington, DC 20223

Think and Grow Rich (cassette)
Success Motivation
5000 Lakewood Dr
Waco, TX 76710

Mutual Fund Series
Investment Company Inst.
1775 K ST
Washington, DC 20006

Information Packet For
Businesswomen
National Assn of Women
Business Owners
500 N Michigan Ave, Suite 1400
Chicago, IL 60611

Tickets For TV Shows - ABC
Guest Relations
7 West 66th
NY, NY 10023

Tickets For TV Shows - NBC
Guest Relations
30 Rockefeller Plz
NY, NY 10020

Tickets For TV Shows - NBC
Guest Relations
3000 W Alameda Ave
Burbank, CA 91523

Tickets For TV Shows - CBS Publicity
51 West 52nd St
NY, NY 10019

Tickets of TV Sows - CBS Publicity
7800 Beverly Blvd
Los Angeles, CA 90036

Applied Photography
Eastman Kodak
343 State St
Rochester, NY 14650

K2R Stain-Dial
Texize Chemicals
Public Relations
Box 368
Greenville, SC 29602

Our Flag
Annin Co. 163 Bloomfield Ave
Verona, NJ 07044

Space Booklets
Public Affairs
JFK Ctr
Cape Canaveral, FL 32899

Shuttle Glider Kit
Public Affairs Office
JFK Space Center, FL 32899

Anti-Smoking Kit
American Lung Assn
1740 Broadway
NY, NY 10019
Lightning Book

National Oceanic & Atmosphere Administration
Central Logistics Supply Center
619 Hardesty St
Kansas City, MO 64124

Diet Recipe Booklet
(Include self-addressed stamped envelope)
Columbo Dept ZW
Methuen, MA 01844

How to Plan Your Wedding Photographs
Eastman Kodak
Dept 412
343 State St
Rochester, NY 14650

Free Racing Decals
Hooker Headers Free Decal Offer
PO Box 1010
1032 West Brooks St
Ontario, CA 91762

Free Fostex Sample For Skin Problems
Westwood Pharmaceuticals
468 Dewitt St
Buffalo, NY 14213

Pasta Primer Recipes
National Pasta Assn
Box 1008
Palatine, IL 60067

If You Want to Give Up Cigarettes
(Put the word FREE on outside of envelope)
Consumer Information
Pueblo, CO 81009

Your Science Project
Edmund Scientific Co.
Barrington, NJ 08007

Home Eye Test
National Society for Prevention of
Blindness
79 Madison Ave
Indianapolis, IN 46222

Racing Decals
Pennzoil Company
Customer Service
1630 W Olympic Blvd
Los Angeles, CA 90015

Racing Decals
Stewart-Warner
Consumer Service Dept
1826 Diversity Parkway
Chicago, IL 60614

Turry Talks About Medicine
Coloring Book
Aetna Special Services Librarian
151 Farmington Ave
Hartford, CT 06156

Touring Service Kit
Exxon Touring Service
PO Box 307
Florham Park, NJ 07932

Unisol Sample
(For soft lens wearers)
CooperVision Pharmaceuticals,
Inc
455 E Middlefield Road
Box 52
Mountain View, CA 94043

Plastic Container for Tampons
Johnson & Johnson
O.B. Purse Pak
Box 76P
Baltimore, MD 21230

The Marry-Go-Round
(Planning a Wedding)
Gingiss Formal Wear
180 North LaSalle St
Chicago, IL 60601

English Muffin Recipes
SB Thomas
930 N Riverview Dr
Totowa, NJ 07512

"Virginia is For Lovers"
Bumper Sticker
Virginia State Travel Service
6 North Sixth St
Richmond, VA 02254

Skillcraft Rug Kit
Skillcraft
500 N Calvert
Baltimore, MD 21202

How to Make & Use a
Pinhole Camera
Eastman Kodak
Photo Information, Dept. 841
343 State St
Rochester, NY 14650

Indian & Eskimo Arts & Crafts
Indian Arts & Crafts
Room 4004
U.S. Dept of the Interior
Washington, DC 20240

Myoflex Creme Free Sample
Myoflex Sample Offer
Warren-Teed Labs
Box 2450
Colombus, OH 43215

Calorie Counter & Carbohydrate Guide
Hollywood Diet Bread
1747 Van Buren St
Hollywood, CA 33020

How Oil Was Formed Chart
Public Relations
Union Oil
Box 7600
Los Angeles, CA 90054

Steps to Buying a Home #12
Bank of America
Specialized Services Dept 3401
P.O. Box 37128
San Francisco, CA 94137

What is a Boy Essay
New England life
501 Boylston St
Boston, MA 02117

What is a Girl Essay
New England Life
501 Boylston St
Boston, MA 02117

Tips on Mounting and Framing
(Include self-addressed stamped envelope)
Eastman Kodak Dept 841
343 State St
Rochester, NY 14650

Free Vitamin Offer
Golden Tabs Pharmaceutical Co
6045 West Howard St
Niles, IL 60648

Michael Recycle Comic
Reynolds Aluminum Co
Box 27003
Richmond, VA 23261

A Freight Train Comes to My House Poster
Assn of American Railroads
Office of Information
1920 "L" St NW
Washington, DC 20036

Metric Conversion Chart
Consumer Relations
Eli Lily & Co
307 McCarty St
Indianapolis, IN 46285

The U.S. Government Oil and Gas Lottery #604K
(Put the word FREE on the outside of the envelope)
Consumer Information
Pueblo, CO 81009

Our Daily Bread Inspirational Reading
Radio Bible Class
P.O. Box 22
Grand Rapids, MI 49555

Creating With Saran Wrap
Dow Chemical Co
Consumer Service
Townsend St
Midland, MI 48640

Carving Guide For Carving Meats
Cutco Cutlery, Dept 33
Wear-Ever Aluminum Co.
1089 Eastern Ave
Chillecothe, OH 45601

How the Heart Works Puzzle
American Heart Association
205 East 42nd St
NY, NY 10017

Peking Review Magazine
Permanent Mission of the
People's Republic of China to the
United Nations
155 W 66th St
NY, NY 10023

Braille Alphabet & Numeral Card
American Foundation For the
Blind
15 West 16th St
NY, NY 10011

Steel: A Picture Story
Bethlehem Steel Co
Bethlehem, PA 18016

Exceptional Black Scientists
Posters
Consumer Relations
CIBA-GEIDGY Co
Ardsley, NY 10502

Sweet Memory Collection Recipe
Cards
Sweet Memory Collection
Sunland Marketing
PO Box 2268
Menlo Park, CA 94025

Emergency Telephone Number
Card
Travelers Insurance
Womens Information Bureau
One Tower Square
Hartford, CT 06115

Smokey the Bear Fire Ranger Kit
Smokey's Kit
Smokey Bear Headquarters
Washington, DC 20252

Nutrients and Foods For Health
Poster
USDA Food and Nutrition Service
Rm 4122
Auditor's Building
Washington, DC 20250

Your Body and How it Works
(For kids ages 6 to 9)
American Medical Assn
Dept of Health Education
5350 N Dearborn
Chicago, IL 60610

Energy Conservation Poster,
Captain America & The Campbell
Kids Poster, Energy Activities
With Energy Ant (For kids)
All From:
Department of Energy
Box 82
Oak Ridge, TN 37830

Free First Aid Guide & Calendar
International Brotherhood of
Electrical Workers
1125 15th St NW
Washington, DC 20005

Ballad of Woodsy Owl Song Sheet
Woodsy owl
Forest Service
PO Box 2417
Washington, DC 20013

How to Respect and Display Our Flag
Publications
U.S. Marine Corps
Department of the Navy
Washington, DC 20360

Leonardo Da Vinci
IBM
Old Orchard Road
Armonk, NY 10504

It's Elementary, My Dear Watson Poster
Sherlock Poster
National Pork Council
Box 10370
Des Moines, IA 50306

Lazy Bones Bumper Sticker
Juvenile Shoe
7700 Clayton Rd
St Louis, MO 63117

Health Today Free Subscription
Health Today
17255 Redford Ave
Detroit, MI 48219

VD - A Fact of Life
Ortho Pharmaceutical Co
Raritan, NJ 08869

Clearasil Sample
Clearasil Deep Pore Cleanser
Sample Offer
Box 3200
Marshfield, WI 54449

The Story of Checks Cartoon
Federal Reserve Bank of New York
33 Liberty St
NY, NY 10045

Bicycle Safety Posters
U.S. Consumer Product Safety Commission
Washington, DC 20207

Get That Bug Poster
Bug Poster
Johnson Wax
Racine, WI 53403

Free Glass Jigger
(Enclose $.25 for postage)
Holland House
Box 1647
Pittsburg, PA 15230

Grecian Formula Sample
Combe, Inc
1101 Westchester Ave
White Plains, NY 10604

Klutch Trial Sample
(For denture wearers)
Klutch Handy Trial Size
I. Putnam
Box 444
Big Flats, NY 14814

Futurific Newsletter
(Ask for sample copy)
Futurific, Inc
280 Madison Ave., Suite 1211
New York, NY 10016

Happy Days Tobacco
Sample Offer
Smokeless Tobacco
1100 W Putnam Ave
Greenwich, CT 06830

Best of Helpful Hints
(inlude self-addressed stamped
envelope)
Mary Ellen Enterprises
6414 Cambridge St
St Louis Park, MN 55426

In Focus Newsletter
(For the young visually
handicapped)
Seeing Clearly
(For adults) Both from:
National Assn For Visually
Handicapped
305 E 24th St
NY, NY 10010

Trucks and Buses Serve America
Poster
Motor Vehicle Manufacturers
Assn
300 New Center Bldg
Detroit, MI 48202

This is Trucks (Game)
Motor Vehicle Manufacturers
Assn
300 New Center Bldg
Detroit, MI 48202

So You'd Like to Adopt a
Wild Horse # 634-H
(Put FREE on the outside of
envelope)
Consumer Information Center
Pueblo, CO 81009

The Principal Rivers & Lakes
 of the World
U.S. Department of Commerce
National Ocean Survey # 0513
Rockville, MD 20852

Story of Environment and Industry
Poster
United States Steel Company
600 Grant St
Pittsburgh, PA 15230

George Washington & the
American Revolution
Washington National Insurance
Co
Evanston, IL 60201

Life Saving Kit
Institute of Makers of Explosives
1575 Eye St, Suite 550
Washington, DC 20005

The Children's Zoo
Eli lily
Public Relations Services
307 E McCarty St
Indianapolis, IN 46285

Johnson's Baby Lotion Sample
Johnson's Baby Lotion
PO Box 14043
Baltimore, MD 21268

Free Plastic 6-Inch Ruler
ILGWU
Union Label Department
275 Seventh Ave - 5th Floor
New York, NY 10001

For Boys: A Book About Girls
Personal Products
Consumer Information Center
Milltown, NJ 08850

Canadian Recipe Collection
Canada Department of Agriculture
Ottawa, Canada
K1A OC7

Land of Adventure Magazine
Royal Norwegian Embassy
2720 34th St NW
Washington, DC 20008

Soviet Life Magazine
Embassy of the U.S.S.R.
1706 18th St, NW
Washington, DC 20009

Sky and Telescope Magazine
Sky Publishing Co.
49 Bay St Rd
Cambridge, MA 02138

The American Buffalo
U.S. Department of the Interior
Fish and Wildlife Service
Washington, DC 20240

Dolls to Make
(Include self-Addressed stamped envelope)
Good Housekeeping Bulletin Service
Box 5174, FDR Station
NY, NY 10150

Crafty Critters Craft Booklet
Texize Chemicals
Box 368
Greenville, SC 29602

The Art of Color Dyeing Chart
Art of Color Dyeing Box 307
Coventry, CT 06238

Collect free money from the U.S. Government
    Uncle Sam doles out a tremendous amount of free money to organizations, businesses, and individuals. Why shouldn't YOU get in on this bonanza?   The sources listed below are only some of the many programs.

    Much of the money that Uncle Sam hands out does not go directly to individuals, but to state agencies and organizations that then distributes it to individuals. Check out your state agencies to find out about that bonanza.

Agriculture Conservation Program 202-447-6221
For control of erosion, pollution, improve water quality, energy conservation, etc. on your farm or ranch.

Cotton Production Stabilization 202-447-7951
To attract cotton production - for owner, landlord, tenant, sharecropper on a farm.

Dairy Indemnity 202-447-7997
To indemnify dairy farmers for losses by pesticide contamination.

Emergency Conservation Program 202-447-6221
For emergency conservation measures on your farm or ranch land.

Forestry Incentives Program 202-447-6221
To bring your private forest land under management.

Agricultural Research - Competitive Research Grants
703-4235-2628   202-475-5022
To promote research in food, agriculture, related areas.

Very Low Income Housing Repair 202-382-7967
To make essential repairs to your rural house to make it safe and

sanitary (very low income).

Anadromous and Great Lakes Fishing Conservation
202-634-7218
Any interested person proposing a cooperative for the conservation of anadromous fish and spawning fish of the Great Lakes and for the control of sea lampreys.

Economic Development - Public Works Impact Program
202-377-3081
For your public or private non-profit organization representing a redevelopment or economic development center to provide meaningful work for unemployed or underemployed.

Financial Assistance for Marine Pollution Research
301-443-8734
To determine ecological consequences of industrial, municipal, and other waste dumped into ocean.

Fisheries Development and Utilization Research and Development Grants and Cooperative Agreements Program
202-634-7451
To develop and strengthen U.S. fishing industry and supply fish to the consumer.

Minority Business Development - Management and Technical Assistance 202-377-2065
To provide free management and technical assistance to you if you are economically and/and or socially depressed and need help starting and/or operating a business.

Selected Reserve Educational Assistance Program
202-697-4334
To stimulate your interest in enlistment into the selective service (non-prior service).

Handicapped Media Services and Captioned Film 202-732-1172
Assistance for your organizations or group to establish captioned film, instructional media, cultural and vocational enrichment, etc. for the handicapped.

Pell Grant Program 800-638-6700 (Maryland 800-492-6602)
For undergraduate students enrolled in institutions of higher learning

Alcohol and Drug Abuse Education Program 202-472-7960
For organizations to develop local capability to solve alcohol and drug abuse problems.

Bilingual Vocational Instructional Materials, Methods, Techniques 202-447-9227
To assist you or your organization to develop instructional materials and research programs and demonstration projects.

Fulbright-Hays Training Grants - Doctoral Dissertation Research Abroad 202-245-2761
For U.S citizens, nationals, or permanent residents to engage in full time dissertation research abroad.

Fulbright-Hays Training Grants - Faculty Research Abroad
202-245-2761
For U.S. educators experienced in a foreign language and area studies.

Graduate and Professional Opportunities 202-245-2347
For an individual accepted by an approved accredited institution for an advanced degree.

Indian Education - Adult Indian Education 202-245-8020
For Indian tribes and organizations to plan, develop, and implement programs for Indian adults.

Indian Education - Fellowships for Indian Students
202-245-8020
For American Indians accepted at an institution of higher education (engineering, medicine, law, business, forestry).

Legal Training for the Disadvantaged 202-245-2347
For low income or economically disadvantaged to attend law school.

Women's Educational Equity 202-245-7965
To promote educational equity for girls and women.

Energy Related Inventions 202-252-9104
To provide assistance to inventors (individuals or entrepreneurs) in developing non-nuclear energy technology and energy-related projects.

Industrial Energy Conservation 202-252-2193
For businesses and organizations to increase efficiency of energy use

and the use of alternative fuels.

Minorities Honors Vocational Training 202-252-8383
To provide scholarship funding to needy minority honor students pursuing vocational training in the energy-related technologies.

Medicare - Hospital Insurance 301-594-9000
To provide hospital care for persons over 65 and certain disabled persons.

Social Security Disability Insurance 301-592-3000
To replace a part of earnings lost for a disabled worker, dependent children, spouse.

Social Security Retirement Insurance 301-592-3000
To replace part of earnings lost because of retirement.

Social Security Survivors Insurance 301-592-3000
To replace part of earnings lost to dependents because of a worker's death.

Special Benefits for Disabled Coal Miners 301-592-3000
To replace some of the income lost to coal miners disabled with black lung disease. Benefits also available to dependent survivors.

Supplemental Security Income 301-592-3000
To provide supplemental income to person 65 and over and to persons blind or disabled whose incomes are low.

Interest Reduction - Homes For Lower-Income Families
202-755-6720
For families - to increase homeownership opportunities for lower-income families.

Lower Income Housing Assistance Program 202-755-5597
To aid lower income-families in obtaining decent housing.

Mortgage Insurance - Rental Housing For The Elderly
202-755-6223
To provide good quality rental housing for the elderly.

Indian Social Services - Child Welfare Assistance
202-343-6434

To provide foster home care for dependent, neglected, and handicapped Indian children.

Indian Social Services - General Assistance 202-343-6434
To provide assistance for living needs to needy Indians.

Indian Education - Higher Education Grant Program
202-343-7387
To encourage Indian students to continue their education and training beyond high school.

Indian Employment Assistance 202-343-3668
To provide vocational training and employment opportunities for Indians.

Indian Housing Assistance 202-343-4876
To provide housing for Indians meeting the income criteria.

Longshoremen and Harbor Workers' Compensation
202-523-8721
For longshoremen, harbor workers, and other maritime workers to provide compensation for occupational disability or death.

Trade Adjustment Assistance - Workers 202-376-6896
To provide adjustment assistance to workers adversely affected by increase of imports directly competitive with employee's firm.

Air Pollution Control Grants 202-382-5744
To promote research and development projects concerning air pollution.

Environmental Protection - Consolidated Research Grants 202-382-5744
To support environmental research by people with high scientific ability.

Safe Drinking Water Research and Demonstration Grants
202-382-5529
To conduct research relating to safe drinking water.

Solid Waste Disposal Research Grants 202-382-5744
To conduct research and development relating to the collection, storage, utilization, salvage, or disposal of solid waste.

Toxic Substances Research Grants 202-382-5744
To promote research relating to the effects, prevention, and control of toxic substances.

National Fire Academy Student Stipend Program 301-447-6771
To provide stipends to students attending Academy courses and programs.

Disaster Assistance 202-646-3615
To provide assistance in federally declared disaster areas.

Grants for the promotion of the Arts
Promotion of the Arts - Dance 202-682-5435
Promotion of the Arts - Design Arts 202-682-5437
Promotion of the Arts - Folk Arts 202-682-5449
Promotion of the Arts - Literature 202-682-5451
Promotion of the Arts - Media Arts 202-682-5452
Promotion of the Arts - Museums 202-682-5442
Promotion of the Arts - Music 202-682-5445
Promotion of the Arts - Theater 202-682-5425
Promotion of the Arts - Visual Arts 202-682-5448
Nation Endowment for the Arts
- Information Office - 202-682-5400

Grants for the promotion of the Humanities
Promotion of the Humanities - Basic Research 202-786-0207
Promotion of the Humanities - Travel 202-786-0207
Promotion of the Humanities - Fellowships 202-786-0466
Promotion of the Humanities - Conferences 202-786-0207
Promotion of the Humanities - Reference Works 202-786-0210
Promotion of the Humanities - Translations 202-786-0210
Promotion of the Humanities - Preservations 202-786-0204
Promotion of the Humanities - Summer Stipends 202-786-0466
National Endowments for the Humanities
- Information officer - 202-786-0438

Engineering Grants - 202-357-9774
To strengthen engineering and applied science research base.

Minority Research Initiation - 202-357-7350
To help minority scientists develop greater research capabilities.

Visiting Professorships for Women - 202-357-7734
To promote the active participation in research and teaching by women
who hold doctorates in science or engineering.

National Science Foundation
- Policy Officer (Information) - 202-357-7880
- Grants for Scientific Research Guidelines - 202-357-7861

Educational Exchange - Graduate Students - 212-883-8200
To promote educational exchanges.

Educational Exchange - Professors and Research Scholars - 202-833-4950

Win at the slots
Most slot machines have three reels. So how many combinations
are possible? That depends upon the number of symbols on each reel.

How often can you expect three bells?

The minimum combinations on a three reel slot are perhaps 20
symbols per reel or 8000 combinations (20 times 20 times 20).
So theoretically a certain winning combination would, on the
average, appear once in every 8000 spins of the reels.
Choose the best odds
But each machine can be set for a rate of payback. The usual
rate on quarter slots is 86 to 90 percent. Let's say a quarter machine
has a payback of 90 percent. That machine would pay back 90
quarters for every 100 quarters dropped into it.
The best odds are on the dollar slots. They are often set to pay
between 97 and 99 percent.
Progressive Games - play the maximum or nothing
The progressive slots are linked together. Each coin dropped in
any of the linked-up machines increases the size of the jackpot.
Unless you play the maximum number of coins, you have no
chance at the progressive jackpot. And the smaller prizes are paid less
often - the odds of winning the smaller prizes are reduced by the large
progressive payoff.
So unless you are willing to put in the maximum and go for the
jackpot, don't play the progressives.

Play only what you can afford to lose
Start out with a bankroll you can afford to lose. Keep these coins

separate from any other money, including your winnings. If necessary, don't bring any other cash with you and leave your checkbook at home.
Play all your start-up coins. Now tally up your winnings.

If you have more than you started with

If your winnings are more than your original bankroll, put your start-up amount in your pocket. Then put an additional percentage in with it - maybe 10 percent.

Use the remaining coins for your new bankroll and begin another round. In each round, you will pocket half the winnings.

If you have less than you started with

If your winnings in the first round are less than your original bankroll, go to a different machine. Using ONLY these coins, start over.

First round winner goes home a winner

As you can see, if you come out ahead in the first round and stick to the method, you will go home a winner. After the first round you will be playing strictly on winnings.

First round loser still could win

If you don't come out a winner on the first round, you still have a chance to win, and you will lose no more than your original bankroll - the amount you decided you could afford to lose.

You will never lose more than you can afford to lose

If you stick with the plan, you will never lose more than you can afford to lose. And you will consistently go home with more in your pocket than you did before.

Stay in control

But you must stay in control - this method works only if you don't change your rules in the middle of the game.

Slot Clubs

Slot clubs are becoming a popular way to play progressive slots for odds. Each member contributes an equal predetermined amount - make sure it is an amount each of you can afford to contribute regularly.

Then members track the progressive games - you should track them for a while BEFORE you make attempts to win them. Keep records so you learn the characteristics of each progressive game. From these records, your team decides at what point each game is pregnant for a payoff.   When the jackpot of a given progressive reaches that predetermined point, a team of members uses the club bankroll and plays until they win or go broke. The key to winning here is to accurately gauge the payoff point.

Win at Bingo

Bingo is a very popular entertainment - some 30 million players in the United States! In addition, it is the major fund-raiser for many religious, social, and charitable groups.

Bingo is a lot of fun but...

Did you know your odds of winning at bingo are less than winning at the slots?   The payback average is only about 60% for bingo. The average for slots is 96%.

Fortunately there is a way to increase your odds so you can win more consistently as well as have fun.

Playing with numbers

Every bingo card has 24 numbers. So if you play one card you will be playing with only 24 numbers; with two cards, you will have 48 possible numbers; with three,72; and with four, 96.

Note the word possible. If the numbers are duplicated on your cards, you are playing with less numbers. For example, if all the cards were identical, you would be playing with only 24 numbers no matter how many cards you played.

Of course, they wouldn't all be identical. But four cards selected at random will have many duplicate numbers. You may be playing with only two thirds of the possible numbers! Why not make the odds better?

Choosing card combinations

Pick cards with as many different numbers as possible. When choosing cards, line them up vertically and run your eye down each column. With four cards, you will have 96 numbers. Since there are only 75 numbers in bingo, you'll necessarily have a few duplicates.

Your objective is to have all of the 75 numbers represented on your four cards. This may seem difficult at first, but give yourself plenty of time and do the best you can. With a little practice, soon you'll be choosing your cards quickly and easily.

Assessing individual cards

Look closely at a bingo card. Because it has a "free" space in the center, there are four positions that require only four numbers to win in regular bingo - one vertical, one horizontal, and two diagonal. These are your "easy win" positions. These four positions account for 90% of wins.

By concentrating on the "easy win" lines, you can increase your odds of winning. Within these lines, try to get a balance of numbers.

Look at the ending digits. Try to get a mix of ending digits plus a balance of odd and even numbers in addition to not duplicating your other cards.

There are only an average of 12 calls per regular bingo game. Of the first 10 calls in any game, most will have different digit endings.

How many cards to play

Do you think that if you play eight cards instead of four, your odds of winning are doubled? Not so! Actually, your chances of winning increase only slightly.

When you consider the extra cost for the extra cards, it isn't worth it! You are better off playing four good, well chosen cards.

Gauge your spending by the payoff

Compare your cost of playing to the average regular prize offered. If your cards cost more than one average win, you are setting yourself up to come out a loser even if you win!

For example, if the average prize for a regular game is $10, don't spend more than $10 for the regular cards for the whole evening.

On specials, use a 30 to 1 odds equation. In other words, spend only one dollar for each $30 in prizes.

For example, if the prize is $15 for a special, you should not spend more than $.50 for that game.

Coverall or Blackout

When 57 or more numbers are called for the jackpot, the odds are excellent that someone will win the game. Therefore, you should increase the number of cards you play at that point. If you can keep up comfortably, you may even want to double the number of cards.

Playing the probabilities

Bingo is gambling - a game of chance. As such it is subject to the laws of probability. This method is an easy, painless method of playing the probabilities.

Using these suggestions, you will not win all of the time, but you will go home a winner more consistently.

Words of truth

Truth is more than a virtue; it is the basis of communication.

Imagine how difficult it would be to pass and receive information and messages if you could never be sure you could trust anyone! Yet we all know we can't trust everyone - at least not all of the time.

A Balancing Act

So you attempt a balancing act. On one hand, you try not to suspect someone is lying. On the other, you try not to "fall for" a lie and appear gullible.

Wouldn't it be nice to take some of the guessing out of the act? Well, actually you can.

Macro alert signals

When lies start to come out of the mouth, the body sends out signals. Some of the major body signals that should alert you are hand-face motions while speaking, such as:

Covering or partially covering the mouth.
Lightly rubbing or touching the nose.
Rubbing the eyes or just under the eyes.
Scratching the neck below the ear lobe.
Rubbing or playing with the ear.

Signals, not evidence

Remember, these gestures are not evidence of lying. But they should put you on guard. They are likely indications of deceit, uncertainty, exaggeration, or apprehension. And a practiced liar will probably be able to suppress some of them. Yet, while consciously suppressing the macro-gestures may be possible, micro-gestures are more difficult to control.

Micro signals

In addition to the major hand-face signals, watch for:

Averted eyes - avoidance of eye contact.
Facial twitches.
Flushed cheeks.
Increased eye blinking.
Expansion or contraction of pupils.
Facial perspiration.

Open Palm

The value of the open palm is recognized by courts of law. When swearing to tell the truth, an open palm is held up. The open palm means truth.

When someone is lying, they tend to conceal their palms - or even their entire hands. The open palm association with openness and honesty is so ingrained it poses problems for even a practiced liar. When he deliberately displays his palms while lying, he will probably be unable to suppress other negative gestures.

Reversing heart disease

Yes, some of the effects of heart disease can be reversed. And it can be done naturally. Since the problem has usually been brought on by your life-style, the reversal will require a change in life-style.

(1) If you smoke, quit.

(2) Limit your alcohol consumption to two drinks or less per day.

(3) Eat a healthy low-fat, low-sugar, low-cholesterol diet. Avoid dairy products, fats, egg yolks, fried foods, tropical oils. The purposes of this diet are reducing your cholesterol level and your body weight.

(4) Go for a brisk walk every day. BUT CHECK WITH Y O U R DOCTOR FIRST. The best exercise for your heart is walking. You should walk at least a mile a day, but work up to it gradually. Walking helps to keep your weight down, strengthens your heart, lowers your cholesterol level, and helps to reduce stress.

(5) Practice positive living. This includes reducing stress, increasing relaxation, and learning to communicate and share your feelings.

Learn to look at things in a positive manner. It may take some time to achieve this, but you can do it. When you are relaxed and and doing something positive about regaining your health, you will feel more positive about life. To achieve a positive attitude, you must also work on your relationships. Don't try to change or control the people around you. Learn to accept them for what they are. The change has to be in you. Learn to open up and share your feelings, communicate. Join a support group that encourages you to share feelings. Surprisingly,happy and open relationships play a very large role in recovery and survival after heart disease.

Premature ejaculation

To control premature ejaculation, try a woman-on-the-top position. Muscle tenseness sometimes plays a role in the problem. When you are on the bottom, you can be more relaxed and be responsible for less of the movements.

Call your nearest sex therapy center. No, it's not the extensive lay-on-the-couch-and-talk-about-your-childhood type of therapy.

It's easy and quick - just a few weeks. You are taught to know your body signals and how to control your ejaculations.

You may even be able to arrange for the therapy to be done by phone.

Diabetes complications

Complications of diabetes in the heart, eyes, kidneys, nervous system, and feet are linked to cholesterol blockages in the blood vessels.

Recent studies indicate that vitamin E may help in preventing these complications by intercepting cholesterol and unstable oxygen molecules that damage artery walls.

Supplements of vitamin A, B6, C, and niacin are also recommended.

Headaches

Headaches are often due to stress and tension. Exercising regularly is one of the best antidotes to stress and tension.

Among the foods that most commonly cause headaches are chocolate, caffeine, and red wine. Also avoid foods that contain the additives monosodium glutamate, nitrites, and nitrates. Avoid very low calorie diets, and get plenty of rest.

The herb feverfew, vitamin C, the B complex vitamins, calcium, magnesium, and potassium are recommended.

Tinnitus

Ginko dilates arteries, veins, and capillaries increasing blood flow to the brain. Therefore, it will help to alleviate hearing loss due to tinnitus, as well as vascular problems and improving memory functions.

Memory loss

Often memory loss is linked to cholesterol buildup. Your brain needs the "food" your blood brings to it, and the sluggish blood flow caused by cholesterol build-up isn't bringing that "food" fast enough.

A low-fat and low-cholesterol is important, because it discourages cholesterol build-up .

Aerobic exercise strengthens your heart so it will pump better as well as lowering your cholesterol.

Niacin, a vitamin you can buy at any pharmacy, improves your blood flow and will help to wake up your memory facilities.

Ginkgo, an herb of Chinese origin, has been shown to dilate

arteries, veins, and capillaries.

Ginseng tea lowers cholesterol and stimulates the cardiovascular system.

Mental Acuity and Mood Foods

Your mood, alertness, memory, and clarity of thought are all directly related to what you eat.

A lot of people feel that "everything I put in my mouth goes to my hips," but truly everything you put in your mouth goes to your brain. What you eat has a powerful effect on your brain processes.

Sugars and starches increase serotonin in your brain. Serotonin is a neurotransmitter that soothes and calms you, reduces your energy and alertness, and reduces your mental acuity.

You digest foods high in fat and cholesterol slowly. This diverts blood from the brain and reduces your mental alertness.

So what does this mean in terms of actual food? Well, let's take your breakfast for example:

Do you like pancakes and syrup or sweet rolls for breakfast? You are eating sugars and starches. You're dampening your energy, and probably won't reach your natural morning energy peak.

Do you prefer bacon and eggs? These foods are high in fat and cholesterol. You're reducing your mental acuity.

With either of these breakfasts, you're obviously not going to feel your best or operate at your peak.

Well, what should you eat for breakfast, then? Try lean ham instead of bacon. Choose a low-fat riccota or cottage cheese instead of butter. Since the natural fructose sugar in fruits does not have the effect of cane or corn sugar or honey, substitute fresh fruit or juice instead of syrups and sugary foods.

What about your morning coffee? Good news for coffee drinkers! One or two cups of coffee or tea will increase your mental alertness, but three or more can cause overstimulation - you'll become less sharp and clear-headed.

How's your lunch? Can you pep up your afternoon with your lunch menu?

If your lunch is heavy on breads, pasta, potatoes, and sweet deserts (high carbohydrate), you may become calmer, but also sleepy, lethargic, and less able to concentrate on your work.

Go for protein rich lunches - like poultry or fish - for alertness and to counteract confusion, indecisiveness, and anxiety and depression. Protein-rich foods pump you up with amino acids in your bloodstream. One of them is tyrosine which converts into dopamine and norepinephrine which promote mental alertness. Fish, meats, soy products, egg yolks, rice, oatmeal, and peanuts (high in choline) will help to stimulate your memory.

For your evening meal, choose the carbohydrates and go easy on the proteins.   Carbohydrates increase the serotonin in your brain soothing and calming you. You become drowsy and less sensitive to pain.   But you need only about 1.5 ounces of carbohydrate for the effect. More will probably make you no calmer - but could make you fatter. A great snack: When you want to be alert - tuna. At bedtime - oatmeal cookies. You are what you eat. Feed your head wisely.

Soap to make your face look younger
You don't need an arsenal of soaps, cleansers, creams, and astringents to keep your face looking younger. Just keep it cleaned and screened - clean and protected from the sun.

How do you clean it
That depends upon your skin type. All types of skin should be cleaned gently. Use a facial cleanser only once or maybe twice a day. Use a gentle cleanser. When you wash your face use your fingertips gently - don't use a washcloth. Blot it dry gently - don't rub it dry.

Oily Skin
If your skin is oily, use a non-moisturizing soap.

Acne-prone skin
For acne-prone skin, use a soap designed especially for acne (a soap with creme added will aggravate acne).

Dry skin
For dry skin use a gentle soap, plain or with creme added. But don't use it every time - use a cold creme to remove make-up between soap washings. The dryness won't cause wrinkles, but will make them more noticeable. There are many moisturizers available - and don't rule out the ones that aren't specifically for the face. Some of the all purpose creams are more effective than so-called face creams.

All skin types
All skin should be protected from the sun. Exposure to the sun can cause mottling, wrinkling, roughening, discoloration, sagging, and cancer. Use a waterfast sunscreen of at least an SPF15 rating. Apply it to your skin liberally. It's best to apply it 15 minutes or so before going outdoors.

Many moisturizers contain sunscreen, but some are not waterproof and some are weak. Some don't even specify how much screening power they have. An SPF of 15 is recommended. If you use a moisturizer with less than 15 SPF, use a sunscreen over it.

Be careful to shade your eyes when you are in the sun. Squinting or other frequent contortions of your face will , over time, cause wrinkles or make those you have deeper.

If you avoid the sun zealously, be sure that your diet includes enough Vitamin-D.

Vitamins

Vitamin supplements vary greatly in price. The high-end of the pricing scale can be two to ten times as much as the low-end. What are you getting for that extra money?

Compare per tablet

When you compare prices of vitamins, figure the price per tablet. Let's say, for example, a bottle of 48 costs $2.99 (.062 per tablet); a bottle of 60 costs $4.50 (.075 per tablet); and a bottle of 100 costs $6.00 (.060 per tablet).

If all tablets are the same strength, your best buy is the bottle of 100. However, if you must take two of that brand to equal one of the others then it would cost you .12 per day making it the most expensive.

Single Supplement Vitamins

When purchasing single supplement vitamins you can easily compare content. If the content is the same, choose the low priced brand - you'll be getting the same benefits.

"Natural" vitamins

Natural vitamin C costs much more but is no more effective than synthetic, so save your money.

Natural vitamin E also costs more, but compared in IUs (international units) natural and synthetic is about the same, so again save your money.

Multivitamin/mineral supplements

Comparing content of multivitamin/mineral supplements is more difficult than comparing single supplements. Fortunately most brands have comparable ingredients.

Some of the more expensive brands claim higher percentages of the RDA of beta carotene, and vitamins E and C. Still if you want the higher percentages, you'd probably do better purchasing the cheapest multi-vitamin and supplementing them with the cheapest single vitamins.

Health claims

Don't be convinced to buy the more expensive vitamins on the basis of health claims. According to the FDA, the only two valid health claims for dietary supplements are the benefits of calcium for osteoporosis and the benefits of folic acid for birth defects.

Go cheap

Why pay two to ten times as much as you have to? Just pick up the bargain brands and save 50% or much more on your vitamins.

PLEASE TELL US WHAT YOU THINK...

Did you enjoy THE BOOK OF POWERFUL SECRETS? Did you find it helpful? Please write your comments below, and thank you.

_____

_____

_____

_____

_____

[ ] Check here if we can use your comments in our advertising with your name, city and state. Please print your name, city and state:

_____   _____
City and State   Release Signature

This book will make a perfect gift for friends or relatives. To receive additional copies of this book, please fill in information below.

50% OFF ORDER FORM

No. of Books_____

Ship To:_____

_____

_____

Please enclose $9.95 per book plus $2 for postage and handling. Send your order form to:

Powerful Secrets
Book Distribution Center
Post Office Box 15196
Montclair, CA 91763-5196

[ ] Total amount enclosed_____

OTHER HEALTH AND MONEY BOOKS

The following books are offered to our preferred customers at a special price.

BOOK	PRICE	
Penny Stock Newsletter (12 issues)	$55.00	*POSTPAID*
Lower Cholesterol & Blood Pressure	$26.95	*POSTPAID*
Proven Health Tips Encyclopedia	$19.97	*POSTPAID*
Foods That Heal	$19.95	*POSTPAID*
Natural Healing Secrets	$26.95	*POSTPAID*
Most Valuable Book Ever Published	$16.95	*POSTPAID*
Eliminate Prostate Problems	$16.95	*POSTPAID*
Drugs-Side Effects	$16.95	*POSTPAID*
Govt. . Benefits For 50 or Over	$26.95	*POSTPAID*
Book of Credit Secrets	$26.95	*POSTPAID*
How To Win At Slot Machines	$30.00	*POSTPAID*
How To Trade Commodities	$149.00	*POSTPAID*
How To Trade Options	$149.00	*POSTPAID*
Money Power	$24.95	*POSTPAID*
Proven Wealth Creating Techniques And Formulas	$19.95	*POSTPAID*

Please send this entire page or write down the names of the books and mail it along with your payment

NAME OF BOOK_____PRICE_____
NAME OF BOOK_____PRICE_____
NAME OF BOOK_____PRICE_____
NAME OF BOOK_____PRICE_____

TOTAL ENCLOSED $_____

SHIP TO:

Name_____

Address_____

City_____ST_____Zip_____

MAIL TO: KEYSTONE PUBLISHING
POST OFFICE BOX 51488
ONTARIO, CA 91761-9827

For other fine books go to our website:

www.emarketupdate.com